How
to
Cook

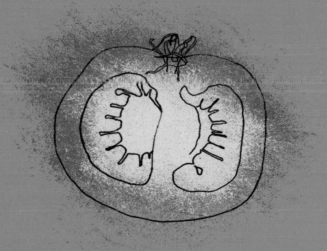

**LONDON, NEW YORK,
MELBOURNE, MUNICH, AND DELHI**

Senior editor Francesca Baines
Senior art editor Sheila Collins
Editors Matilda Gollon, Ashwin Khurana
Designers Hoa Luc, Katie Knutton
Managing editor Linda Esposito
Managing art editor Jim Green

Category publisher Laura Buller
Design development manager Sophia M Tampakopoulos Turner
Development team Laura Brim, Jayne Miller
Senior production controller Angela Graef
Production editor Clare McLean
DK picture library Rob Nunn
Jacket editor Matilda Gollon
Jacket designer Laura Brim

Step illustrations Maltings Partnership
Other illustrations Hennie Haworth, Rosie Scott
Original photography Dave King
Home economist for photography Katy Greenwood

First published in Great Britain in 2011 by
Dorling Kindersley Limited,
80 Strand, London, WC2R 0RL

2 4 6 8 10 9 7 5 3 1
179066 – 01/11

A CIP catalogue record for this book is available
from the British Library.

ISBN 978-1-40536-302-0

Hi-res workflow proofed by MDP, UK
Printed and bound by Hung Hing, China

**Discover more at
www.dk.com**

How to Cook

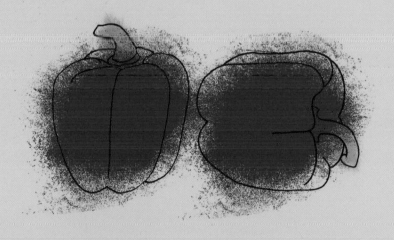

Consultant Maggie Mayhew

Contents

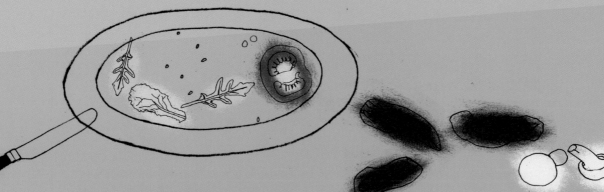

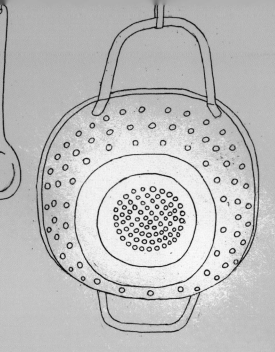

Fun with food

It's time to get cooking. Why? Because food is fun. Get a few people together, add some food, and suddenly you've got a party. It's an important part of every special occasion – birthdays, weddings, and picnics! Another good reason to learn how to cook is that it's a skill for life. You have to eat every day, so why not find out how to cook tasty dishes that you can share with your friends and family?

Confident cooking

If you haven't done it before, cooking can seem a bit daunting, so the recipes in this book explain simply and clearly how to make things. But there are also lots of tips and ideas for variations because, once you've mastered the basic techniques, we hope you'll feel confident enough to adapt recipes yourself, add in your favourite ingredients, and play around with flavours.

Healthy eating

Eating the right food is vital for good health, and every day you need to eat a variety of foods. There are five main food groups, each of which provides an important part of your diet.

Fruits and vegetables

You should eat at least five portions of fruits and vegetables a day. They contain lots of vitamins and minerals, and are a source of fibre, especially if you eat them with their skins on.

Fats and sugars

Your body needs some fat, but too much is bad for you. The best kinds of fats are found in oily fish (such as tuna and salmon), nuts, seeds, avocados, and oils. Sugar provides energy, but too much can lead to obesity and is bad for your teeth.

Carbohydrates

Bread, potatoes, grains, cereals, rice, and pasta give you energy. Wholegrain breads and cereals are higher in fibre and give longer-lasting energy than white bread and processed cereals.

Milk and dairy

Dairy foods such as milk and cheese contain calcium. Your body needs this mineral to keep your bones, teeth, nails, and hair in good repair. Semi-skimmed and skimmed milk contain as much calcium as whole milk but are lower in fat.

Proteins

Protein helps you to grow, builds up your muscles, and keeps you strong. It is found in meat, fish, eggs, nuts, seeds, and pulses (such as peas, beans, and lentils).

A balanced diet

It's important to get the balance of the different foods in your diet right. This plate has been divided up to show the percentage of each type of food you should aim to eat each day.

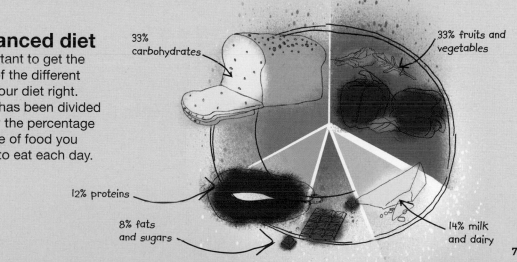

33% carbohydrates

33% fruits and vegetables

12% proteins

8% fats and sugars

14% milk and dairy

In the kitchen

Cooking involves working with heat and using equipment that must be handled with care, such as sharp knives. Common sense, and the guidelines below, will help you to stay safe in the kitchen, but always ask an experienced cook for help if you need it. If you are unsure of any cooking techniques, such as how to prepare a chilli, or separate an egg, turn to the back of the book, where they are explained.

Safety

- Always use oven gloves when handling hot pans, baking trays, and tins.
- Don't put hot pans directly on to the work surface, but use a heat mat, metal rack or trivet, or wooden or heatproof board.
- A sharp knife is safer than a blunt one, but remember that sharp knives should be used carefully and treated with respect.
- Wear an apron to protect your clothes.
- Keep the cooking area clean, and wipe up any spills that could cause accidents.

Hygiene

- Always wash your hands before you start.
- Wash all fruits and vegetables.
- Any chopping board or knife used in the preparation of raw poultry, meat, or fish should be cleaned thoroughly with hot soapy water before using it again.
- Raw eggs carry a risk of contamination from the salmonella bacterium. Do not give foods with uncooked eggs in them to babies and young children, pregnant women, or the elderly.
- Use separate cutting boards for meat and vegetables.
- Always check the use-by dates on ingredients, and don't use them if the date has passed.

Abbreviations

Metric
g = gram
ml = millitre

Imperial
oz = ounce
lb = pound
fl oz = fluid ounces

Spoon measures
tsp = teaspoon
tbsp = tablespoon

Weighing ingredients

- Measure and weigh out all the ingredients before you start cooking.
- Measurements are given in both metric and imperial. Use either one, but don't mix them within a recipe.
- Spoons refer to measuring spoons, not cutlery, and they should be level, not heaped.
- Stand a measuring jug on a flat surface when using it.
- Don't pour ingredients into measuring spoons over the food you are preparing in case it spills into the mixture.

Cook's notes

- Gather and prepare all ingredients before you start cooking – you don't want to discover halfway through a recipe that you have run out of something important.

- All fruits and vegetables listed in recipes are medium sized unless stated otherwise.

- Use medium-sized eggs unless stated otherwise, and free-range if possible.

- Always use the type of flour specified in a recipe – strong, plain, or self-raising.

- It's important to preheat the oven for 10 minutes or so before using it to allow for the correct temperature to be reached.

- Preparation and cooking times are only a guide. Cooking times may vary according to the type of pan, or oven, and the ripeness of ingredients.

- The easiest way to make cooking stock is using a stock cube, or stock powder, and adding the correct quantity of water, according to instructions on the packet.

Food fast

If you find yourself short on time, or get home needing food fast, it doesn't mean you can't eat well, or have to turn to junk food. There are lots of tasty snacks you can rustle up quickly, or cook ahead.

Minestrone

There is nothing quite like a hearty soup to warm the bones on a chilly winter's evening. Minestrone – which literally means "big soup" – is a delicious Italian recipe that combines fresh vegetables, pasta, and aromatic herbs.

SERVES 4
PREPARATION: 30 MINUTES
COOKING: 10 MINUTES

1 tbsp olive oil

1 onion, finely chopped

3 garlic cloves, finely chopped

2 celery sticks, finely chopped

1 large courgette, halved and sliced

150 g (5½ oz) French beans, cut into short lengths

1.3 litres (2¼ pints) hot vegetable stock

2 tsp tomato purée

400 g (14 oz) can cannellini beans, drained

100 g (3½ oz) dried pasta, such as pipe rigate, or macaroni

1 tbsp pesto

salt and freshly ground black pepper

Parmesan cheese

1 Heat the oil in a large, deep pan over a low heat. Add the onion and fry over low heat for 5 minutes, or until soft.

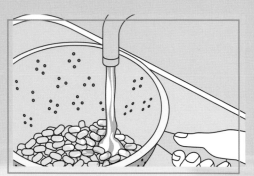

2 Add the garlic, celery, and courgette. Continue to cook over low heat for 10 minutes.

3 Stir in the French beans, vegetable stock, and tomato purée, and bring to the boil. Slightly reduce the heat, then cover and simmer for about 5 minutes.

4 Rinse the cannellini beans in a colander, and add them to the soup with the pasta. Bring the soup to the boil, then simmer for 10 minutes. Stir in the pesto, and season with salt and freshly ground black pepper.

5 Grate some Parmesan cheese over the soup, and serve with lots of hot crusty bread.

For extra flavour, scatter fresh basil leaves or rosemary over the soup.

Beans and bacon

Try different types of beans, such as butter beans or kidney beans, in place of the cannellini. You can even add some diced bacon with the onions for a meaty version.

Gazpacho

This refreshing Spanish chilled soup is perfect for a hot summer's day. Gazpacho was traditionally eaten by peasants and farmers and mainly contained bread, water, and olive oil all pounded together. Tomatoes were not added to the recipe until the 1700s.

Top Tip
Don't overfill the blender in step 3. If you have too much soup, whizz up the mixture in two smaller batches.

SERVES 4

PREPARATION: 30 MINUTES, PLUS CHILLING

1 red pepper, deseeded and finely chopped

1 red onion, finely chopped

1 cucumber, finely chopped

1 kg (2¼ lb) tomatoes, skinned, deseeded, and finely chopped

1 tbsp chopped fresh parsley

100 g (3½ oz) day-old bread, preferably country style

2 garlic cloves, chopped

4 tbsp olive oil, plus extra to serve

3 tbsp red wine vinegar

400 ml (14 fl oz) chilled water

salt and freshly ground black pepper

1 Put the pepper, onion, cucumber, and tomatoes in a mixing bowl with the parsley.

2 Whizz the bread in a blender with the garlic, then add it to the mixing bowl with the olive oil and vinegar. Slowly add the water to give the mixture a thick consistency.

3 Transfer the mixture from the bowl to the blender and whizz for 10 seconds. Don't worry if you can see the odd chunk of cucumber, but if you prefer a smoother soup, blend for a bit longer, adding extra water if the consistency is too thick.

4 Season with salt and freshly ground black pepper. Transfer the soup into a serving dish and place in the fridge for 2–4 hours, until completely cold. To serve, drizzle with olive oil.

If you like a bit of spice, try adding a few drops of Tabasco sauce to the soup before eating.

Keep aside 2 tbsp of chopped vegetables before blending and serve them in the soup as a garnish.

Find out how to skin tomatoes on page 118.

Simple soups

Soups are easy to make, and can be as simple or involved as you like. Enjoy them before a main course, or serve them with lots of crusty bread and turn them into a meal in themselves. To add to the flavour, sprinkle over some tasty toppings, such as crispy bacon bits or cheesy croutes. All recipes serve 4.

Grate Cheddar cheese to melt into the soup.

Pea soup

Cook 4 sliced spring onions in 55 g (2 oz) butter in a saucepan until soft. Add 600 ml (1 pint) vegetable stock and bring to the boil. Add 350 g (12 oz) frozen peas, then simmer for 3–4 minutes. Allow to cool a little, pour into a blender, then whizz until smooth. Return the soup to the saucepan and stir in 150 ml (¼ pint) single cream and 2 tsp chopped fresh mint. Season with salt and freshly ground black pepper.

Small salty pieces of grilled bacon are delicious with pea soup.

Hot tortilla soup

In a pan, cook 1 chopped onion in 1 tbsp olive oil until soft with 1 garlic clove and 1 red chilli, both finely chopped. Add 1 tbsp paprika, 1 litre (1¾ pints) tomato juice, and 300 ml (10 fl oz) vegetable stock, and simmer for 15 minutes. Heat 4 tbsp sunflower oil in a frying pan, add 2 soft corn tortillas, cut into strips, and fry until crisp. Drain on kitchen paper. Stir in 2 tbsp chopped fresh coriander and the juice of 1 lime, season with salt and freshly ground black pepper and top with tortillas.

Roast tomato soup

Roast 12 tomatoes – about 675 g (1½ lb) – with 2 unpeeled cloves of garlic and 3 tbsp olive oil at 200°C (400°F/Gas 6) for about 45 minutes. When cool, squeeze the garlic out of their skins. Meanwhile, chop 1 red onion, 1 potato, and 2 sticks of celery and fry in 1 tbsp olive oil until soft. Add 1 litre (1¾ pints) vegetable stock, 2 tsp sugar, and the roasted tomatoes, and garlic. Simmer for 20 minutes. Blend until smooth, then press through a sieve.

For a bit of crunch, sprinkle over some seeds or nuts.

Crusty garlic bread is great for dipping in soups (see page 36).

Spicy lentil soup

Gently fry 2 onions, 2 celery sticks, and 2 carrots – all finely chopped – in 1 tbsp olive oil. Cook for 5 minutes, then add 2 crushed garlic cloves and 1 tsp curry powder, and stir for a further 1 minute. Add 150 g (5½ oz) red lentils, 1.4 litres (2½ pints) vegetable stock, and 120 ml (4 fl oz) tomato juice. Bring to the boil, then turn down the heat, cover, and simmer for 25 minutes. Season with salt and freshly ground black pepper.

Cheesy croutes (large croutons) are great with soups. Cut baguette into 1 cm (½ in) slices. Toast, then rub the cut side of a halved garlic clove over one side, top with some Cheddar cheese, and grill.

15

Salad Niçoise

This is a great salad if you want something that's quick to make, filling, and really tasty. A speciality of the Côte d'Azur region of France, and named after the city of Nice, Salad Niçoise is full of flavour, with salty anchovies and olives, juicy tuna, and fresh herbs.

SERVES 4
PREPARATION: 30 MINUTES

3 eggs

225 g (8 oz) small new
  potatoes, washed

115 g (4 oz) French beans,
  trimmed

6 small tomatoes, quartered

2 x 200 g (7 oz) can tuna in
  olive oil, drained

handful of fresh flat-leaf
  parsley, chopped

bunch of fresh chives,
  finely chopped

12 black olives, pitted

50 g (1¾ oz) can anchovy
  fillets, drained

1 crisp lettuce, leaves
  separated and washed

For the dressing
6 tbsp olive oil

2 tbsp white wine vinegar

1 garlic clove, halved

2 tsp Dijon
  mustard

salt and freshly
  ground black
  pepper

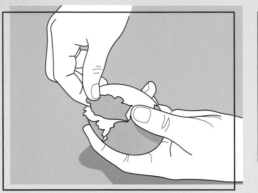

 1 Cook the eggs in a pan of simmering water for about 10 minutes. Cool in cold water and then remove the shells.

2 Boil the potatoes for about 10–15 minutes, or until tender when pierced with a knife. Drain and leave to cool, then cut in half, lengthways. Simmer the French beans in a pan of water for 3 minutes, then drain and cool in cold water.

3 Put the potatoes, beans, tomatoes, tuna, herbs, olives, anchovies, and lettuce leaves in a large serving bowl.

4 Put all the dressing ingredients in a screw-top jar. Season well with salt and freshly ground black pepper. Make sure the lid is on tight, then shake well to mix everything up.

5 Remove the garlic from the dressing, then drizzle it over the salad and gently toss together. Quarter the eggs and arrange them on top. Serve with lots of fresh crusty bread to mop up the juices.

Anchovies are tiny fish preserved in salt to give them a strong, distinctive flavour. If you're not a fan, leave them out.

Assemble the salad just before you're going to eat it – if you leave the vegetables in the dressing for too long, they will lose their freshness and become soggy.

Top Tip

For a treat, use fresh tuna. Fry tuna steaks in a little olive oil for a few minutes on each side, according to how well cooked you like them, and serve on top of the salad.

Pitted olives have had their stones removed.

Cheese, please

If fish is not your thing, replace the tuna with cheese. Try slices of Greek halloumi cheese cooked on a hot griddle pan for 3 minutes on each side, or until it turns golden brown. Or use fresh mozzarella, torn into chunks, with a handful of fresh basil leaves.

Any type of tomato is good, but for a sweeter taste, try cherry tomatoes.

17

Classic salads

These salads taste fantastic and are good for you, too. Best of all, it won't take you long to prepare them. Try and use really fresh ingredients, which will have more flavour. Feel free to make up your own salads, too – even a simple mix of crunchy green salad leaves is delicious with a tasty homemade dressing.

Mozzarella, avocado, and tomato salad tastes delicious with fresh ciabatta bread.

Mozzarella, avocado, and tomato salad (serves 4)

Slice 6 tomatoes, 2 peeled avocados, and 3 125-g (4½-oz) balls buffalo mozzarella and layer onto a plate. Scatter fresh basil leaves over the salad, followed by a sprinkling of salt and plenty of freshly ground black pepper. To serve, drizzle some extra virgin olive oil all over.

Leave the stalk end intact to hold the onion together while you slice off the rings.

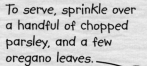

To serve, sprinkle over a handful of chopped parsley, and a few oregano leaves.

Greek salad (serves 4)

Chop 4 tomatoes into wedges and mix in a bowl with ½ a sliced cucumber, ½ a sliced red onion, 1 sliced yellow pepper, and a handful of black olives. Pile on top of some lettuce leaves, and top with 150 g (5 oz) diced feta cheese and a few oregano leaves. Drizzle over 4 tbsp olive oil and a squeeze of fresh lemon juice.

Potato salad (serves 6)

Cook 1¼ kg (2¾ lb) new potatoes in boiling water for 15–20 minutes, or until tender when pierced with a sharp knife. Drain and allow to cool. Mix 4 tbsp mayonnaise with 2 tbsp soured cream and 2 tbsp chopped fresh chives in a large bowl. When the potatoes are cool, cut them into bite-sized pieces. Stir into the mayonnaise mixture.

Season with generous amounts of freshly ground black pepper.

Honey mustard dressing

Spoon 2 tsp wholegrain mustard and 2 tsp honey into a jar, and add a pinch of salt and freshly ground black pepper, ½ finely chopped garlic clove, and 2 tbsp lemon juice. Add 6 tbsp olive oil, screw on the lid tightly, and shake.

This dressing will give your salad a sharp and sweet flavour.

French dressing

Add 2 tbsp white wine vinegar and 2 tsp Dijon mustard to a small jar and shake until well combined. Open the jar, and pour in 6 tbsp extra virgin olive oil, and season with salt and plenty of freshly ground black pepper. Put the lid back on the jar and shake well.

Use the largest holes on the grater.

Coleslaw (serves 6)

To make the dressing, mix 3 tbsp plain yoghurt with ½ tbsp Dijon mustard and 3 tbsp mayonnaise. Finely slice ½ a white cabbage, grate 2 large carrots, and mix with ½ a sliced onion. Place all the vegetables into a large bowl, and stir through the dressing. Season to taste with freshly ground black pepper.

Spanish omelette

In Spain this simple potato omelette is called *tortilla española*. The Spanish eat it all the time, as a snack, in a sandwich, and as tapas – a light meal made up of lots of small, tasty dishes.

Top Tip
Instead of turning the omelette over in step 4, place the pan under a grill on medium-low heat for 5–10 minutes, or until cooked.

SERVES 4
PREPARATION: 30 MINUTES
COOKING: 25–30 MINUTES

200 ml (7 fl oz) olive oil
6 potatoes, about 1 kg (2¼ lb),
  peeled and thinly sliced
5 eggs
salt and freshly ground
  black pepper

1 Heat the olive oil in a deep-sided non-stick frying pan, and add the potatoes. Cook over a low heat for 15 minutes, or until the potatoes are soft, stirring occasionally so that they cook evenly. Turn off the heat, and leave the potatoes to cool.

2 In a large bowl, beat the eggs and plenty of seasoning with a fork. Add the potatoes with a slotted spoon to remove any excess oil. Stir very gently so all the potatoes get coated in the egg mixture, trying not to break them up too much.

3 Heat 1 tbsp of the saved olive oil in a 23-cm (9-in) frying pan, and pour in the potato mixture. Reduce the heat to medium-low and cook for 20 minutes, or until the bottom of the omelette is cooked.

4 Remove from the heat and slide the omelette on to a plate, and then place another plate on top. Gripping them firmly, quickly turn the plates over so the uncooked side is now on the bottom. Slide the omelette back into the pan and cook for about 5–10 minutes, or until cooked through and golden.

5 Allow the omelette to cool in the pan for 5 minutes, then slide it out on to a plate. Leave to cool slightly for another few minutes, then slice into wedges. Serve with salad for a snack, or in a sandwich of crusty bread.

Spanish omelette is delicious served cold, and great for picnics.

Add some extras
If you want a bit of variation, try adding finely chopped onions, chopped peppers, sliced mushrooms, or diced chorizo to the mixture in step 1.

Easy eggs

If you've got some eggs in the fridge, there are lots of quick, tasty snacks you can make for a big breakfast, a light lunch, or a simple meal any time of the day. The ideas below are easy to prepare, delicious, and nutritious, so get cracking! All recipes serve 2.

For a sweeter French toast, use slices of panettone (a type of bread from Italy, pictured) or brioche instead of plain bread, and leave out the salt. Serve with fresh berries and a sifting of icing sugar, or try with any type of jam.

French toast
Whisk 2 eggs with a pinch of salt, then pour into a dish. Add 2 thick slices of bread, leave to soak, and turn over so both sides are coated and all the egg has soaked in. Heat a knob of butter in a frying pan. Cook the bread in the pan. When golden underneath, flip over and cook the other side. Serve sweet with maple syrup and fruit, or savoury with crispy bacon and tomato sauce.

Snip a few fresh chives on to the eggs for a finishing touch.

Smoked salmon and scrambled eggs
Whisk 4 eggs with 2 tbsp milk and some salt and freshly ground black pepper. Melt 15 g (½ oz) butter in a non-stick saucepan over a low heat. Pour in the eggs and stir slowly. When the mixture has formed soft lumps, turn off the heat. The eggs will continue to cook, so slightly undercook them. Butter some toasted bread or bagels and spoon the eggs on top. Top with slices of smoked salmon.

Pipérade

In a frying pan, cook 2 chopped red peppers with 1 sliced onion and 1 finely chopped clove of garlic in 2 tbsp olive oil over a medium heat for about 20 minutes, or until very soft. Add 2 deseeded, chopped tomatoes and 1 tbsp chopped fresh parsley. Cook until the mixture becomes mushy. Season with 1 tsp sugar and some salt and black pepper. Stir in 5 whisked eggs until they start to form soft lumps. This is delicious with hot buttered toast.

To deseed a pepper, cut it in half through the stalk. Use a small sharp knife to cut around the stalk, core, and seeds, then discard them. Scrape out any remaining white pith and seeds.

Huevos rancheros

This is a classic Mexican breakfast – its name means "ranch eggs". Finely chop 1 onion, 1 red pepper, 1 garlic clove, and 1 red chilli and cook with ½ tsp fresh or dried oregano in a frying pan with a little olive oil. Cook for 10 minutes, then add a 400 g (14 oz) can chopped tomatoes, some seasoning, and 1 tsp sweet paprika, and continue to cook for a further 5 minutes. Make 4 hollows in the mixture and break an egg into each. Cover and cook for 3–5 minutes, or until the eggs are cooked. Serve with warmed soft tortillas.

For a meaty version, fry some sliced chorizo sausage in the oil before adding the vegetables. It will give the dish a delicious smoky flavour.

Potato rösti

This classic Swiss dish is made from grated potatoes that are fried until crispy. You can make big pan-sized röstis, but these smaller pancakes are easier to turn. Eat them for breakfast, or as a side dish to a main meal.

Top Tip
For a bit of variety, try adding some extra ingredients to the potato, such as bacon, onion, cheese, or herbs.

MAKES 8 RÖSTI
PREPARATION: 20 MINUTES, PLUS COOLING
COOKING: 10–20 MINUTES

3–4 medium-sized floury
  potatoes, about 800 g
  (1¾ lb), peeled
salt and freshly ground
  black pepper
4 tbsp olive oil

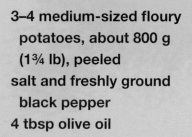

 1 Cut the potatoes in half and parboil them in a saucepan of boiling salted water for 6–7 minutes. Drain and allow to cool.

2 Coarsely grate the potatoes into a bowl – graters with big holes are best.

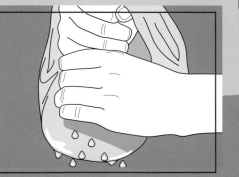

3 Use a clean tea towel to squeeze out any excess liquid, which would make the rösti soggy. Add the salt and pepper, and mix lightly with a fork.

 4 Heat half the oil in a large frying pan and let it begin to sizzle and foam. Shape spoonfuls of the grated potato mixture into round cakes 1–2 cm (½–¾ in) thick and place four cakes into the pan.

5 Gently fry the rösti for about 5–10 minutes, or until golden brown and crisp underneath. Turn them with a spatula or fish slice, then cook for a further 5–10 minutes, or until browned on the other side. Remove from the pan and keep warm while cooking the rest of the mixture in the remaining oil.

One of the best ways to serve rösti is with a fried egg on top.

Mix your veg

Get inventive and mix the potato with some other delicious root vegetables, such as sweet potatoes, carrots, parsnips, or even beetroot.

25

Crêpes

Pancakes come in all shapes and sizes and are eaten in almost every country in the world. In France people make thin pancakes called *crêpes*, which can be sweet or savoury.

Top Tip
If you put in too little batter to begin with, pour in a little extra batter to fill in the gaps to cover the bottom of the pan.

MAKES 8 CRÊPES
PREPARATION: 10 MINUTES
COOKING: 20 MINUTES

125 g (4½ oz) plain flour
1 tsp caster sugar
pinch of salt
2 eggs
300 ml (½ pint) milk
2 tbsp melted butter,
  plus extra for frying

1 Sift the flour into a large bowl and add the sugar and salt. Set aside. In a separate jug, whisk together the eggs and milk.

2 Make a well in the centre of the flour mixture and gradually pour in the egg mixture, beating well until smooth, then stir in the melted butter.

3 Heat a non-stick frying pan over a medium-high heat, and add a little melted butter. Ladle some of the batter into the pan, then tip the pan to spread the batter over the bottom.

4 Cook for 1–2 minutes, or until golden, then flip over with a spatula and cook for another 30 seconds. Set aside on a plate. Repeat until all the batter is used up.

Before rolling, squeeze over some lemon juice and a sprinkling of caster sugar.

Ham and cheese crêpes
Lay a slice of ham on each crêpe, sprinkle with grated cheese, and roll up. Place the crêpes in a buttered frying pan and cook for 1 minute on each side, pressing down on them with a spatula so that the cheese melts.

26

Pancakes

Sometimes called hotcakes or flapjacks in the USA, these small, puffy pancakes are perfect for breakfast. Eat them with butter or smothered with maple syrup and fresh berries.

Top Tip

For fruity pancakes, add a large handful of fresh blueberries, raspberries, or sliced banana to the batter before cooking, and serve with vanilla ice cream.

MAKES 6 PANCAKES
PREPARATION: 10 MINUTES
COOKING: 20 MINUTES

135 g (4¾ oz) plain flour
1 tsp baking powder
½ tsp salt
2 tbsp caster sugar
130 ml (4 fl oz) milk
1 egg
2 tbsp melted butter,
  plus extra for frying

Stack the pancakes and drench them with maple syrup or honey. Serve with fresh strawberries, blueberries, and raspberries.

1 Sift the flour, baking powder, salt, and caster sugar into a large bowl. Lightly beat together the milk and egg in a jug, then whisk in the melted butter.

2 Pour the milk mixture into the flour mixture and, using a balloon whisk, beat until smooth and all the lumps have disappeared. Let the batter stand for a few minutes.

3 Heat a non-stick frying pan over a medium heat and add a little butter. Add a spoonful of batter to the pan, or as many as you can fit, depending on the size of the pan.

4 Cook the pancakes until the tops begin to bubble and they are golden underneath. Flip them over and cook until golden brown on both sides and each pancake has risen to about 1 cm (½ in) thick.

5 Repeat until all the batter is used up. For a real treat, serve with maple syrup and a mixture of berries.

Maple syrup is made from the sap of maple trees.

Falafel

These chickpea patties are a popular Middle Eastern snack. Spicy and delicious, falafel are great for serving up to both vegetarians and non-vegetarians. Full of protein and fibre, they're good for you, too.

MAKES 12 FALAFEL
PREPARATION: 20 MINUTES
COOKING: 6 MINUTES

400 g (14 oz) can chickpeas, drained
½ small onion, chopped
1 garlic clove, chopped
2 tbsp plain flour
1 tsp ground cumin
1 tsp ground coriander
1 tbsp chopped fresh parsley
salt and freshly ground black pepper
200 ml (7 fl oz) sunflower oil

1 Place the chickpeas, onion, garlic, flour, cumin, coriander, parsley, and salt and pepper into a food processor. Blend together until smooth.

2 Lightly sprinkle the work surface with some flour and tip out the mixture from the food processor. Divide it into 12 equal portions and shape each one into a flat, round patty.

3 Pour the sunflower oil into a frying pan over a medium heat. Fry the falafel for about 3 minutes on each side, or until they are crisp and golden.

4 Using a spatula, carefully take out the cooked falafel and place them on a plate lined with kitchen paper to drain any excess oil. Serve warm or cold with salad.

For a little extra zing, squeeze over some lemon juice just *before* serving.

A pitta is an Arabic flatbread that puffs up when it's cooked and then collapses as it cools, creating a "pocket" in the middle that you can open up and fill.

Slice the cucumber and finely shred the lettuce so you can pack lots inside the pitta bread.

Packed pittas

A great way to eat falafel is packed inside pockets of pitta bread. Warm a pitta under the grill, in a toaster, or in the microwave. Slice open, spread a layer of hummus (see page 31) inside, and lie some falafel on top. Throw in some chopped salad vegetables, such as cucumber, tomatoes, lettuce, or spring onions, and a few dollops of tzatziki (see page 30).

Dips and dippers

Here are some super-quick recipes to make when you want something tasty to snack on while you're waiting for the main meal, for friends to arrive, or for the barbecue to get hot. Mix and match these healthy snacks as much as you like… just don't forget to leave some room for the main course! All recipes serve 6.

Potato wedges
Heat the oven to 220°C (425°F/Gas 7). Scrub some large potatoes, pat dry, cut into halves lengthways, and then each half into three pieces. Cook the potatoes in boiling salted water for 5 minutes, then drain. Put in a roasting tin and drizzle with 2 tbsp olive oil, then mix with salt, pepper, and 1 tsp paprika until coated. Bake for about 45 minutes, occasionally shaking the pan, until golden.

There's no need to peel the potatoes – the crispy skins are the best bit.

Guacamole
Use a fork to mash the flesh of 2 ripe, avocados with the juice of 1 lime. Stir in ½ a chopped red onion, 2 chopped tomatoes, 1 deseeded and finely chopped red chilli, and 2 tbsp chopped fresh coriander. Season with salt and freshly ground black pepper.

Use only ripe avocados. To check, hold one in the palm of your hand and squeeze gently – it should give slightly.

Tzatziki
Grate ½ a peeled cucumber, sprinkle with a little salt, and squeeze in kitchen paper to remove excess water. Put the grated cucumber in a bowl and mix in 1 finely chopped garlic clove, 250 g (9 oz) Greek yoghurt, the juice of ½ a lemon, 1 tbsp olive oil, and 1 tbsp chopped fresh mint.

Drain off as much water as you can from the cucumber or the tzatziki will be very liquid.

Hummus

Drain and rinse a 400 g (14 oz) can of chickpeas and tip them into a food processor. Add 2 finely chopped garlic cloves, the juice of 1 lemon, 2 tbsp tahini paste, 3 tbsp olive oil, and a pinch of paprika. Blend until smooth. Serve with a drizzle of olive oil, a sprinkling of paprika, a few chickpeas, and some chopped fresh coriander.

Vegetable sticks

Chop a colourful selection of raw salad vegetables into chunky sticks or strips and use them for dipping – carrots, red, yellow, or orange peppers, celery, and cucumber are all good. They're fresh, crunchy, and healthy, too.

Breadsticks are great for dipping – look out for packs of Italian grissini, which you can keep in the store cupboard.

Tomato salsa

Mix 6 chopped tomatoes, ½ a chopped onion, 1 finely chopped garlic clove, the juice of ½ a lime, 1 finely chopped and deseeded small green chilli, 2 tbsp olive oil, and 2 tbsp chopped fresh coriander. Season with salt and pepper.

The tastiest tomatoes are deep, bright red.

Slice quesadillas in quarters
and eat them while they're
warm and the cheese is still
soft and melted.

Love onions?

Make a delicious vegetarian quesadilla
by leaving out the chicken, slicing an
onion, and cooking it with the pepper
in step 2.

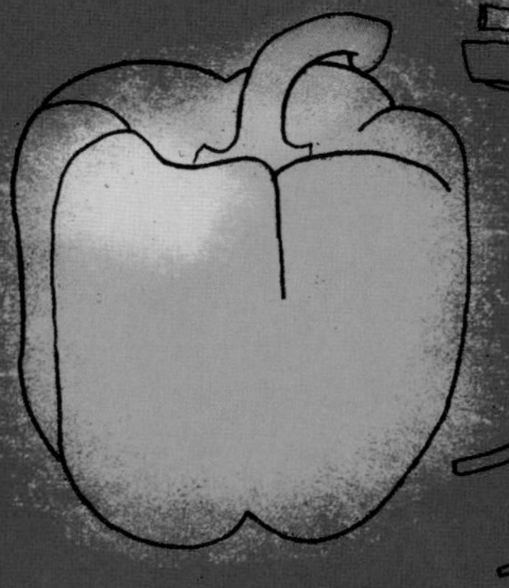

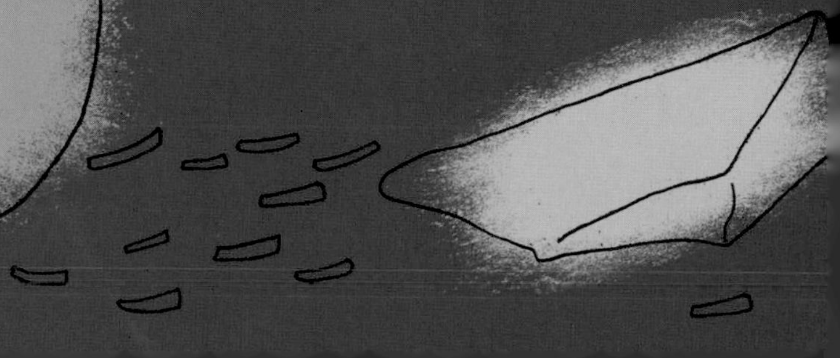

Chicken quesadillas

Queso is Spanish for "cheese", and a quesadilla is really a Mexican version of a toasted cheese sandwich using tortillas – flatbreads made of corn or wheat flour. You can buy prepared tortillas in supermarkets. Make sure you buy soft tortillas, not tacos, which are hard. This recipe adds chicken to the mix.

MAKES 2
PREPARATION: 20 MINUTES
COOKING: 2 MINUTES

2 tbsp olive oil
1 skinned boneless chicken
  breast, sliced
1 red or yellow pepper,
  deseeded and sliced
2 spring onions, sliced
salt and freshly ground
  black pepper
4 soft tortillas
handful of fresh coriander,
  chopped
100 g (3½ oz) mild Cheddar
  cheese, grated

1 Heat 1 tbsp olive oil in a frying pan. Add the chicken strips and cook for 5 minutes, or until beginning to brown.

2 Add the sliced pepper and a pinch of salt to the chicken. Cook for 5 minutes, or until soft. Transfer the mixture to a bowl with the spring onions and some freshly ground black pepper.

4 Top with another tortilla, pressing it down with the back of a spatula to sandwich the two together. After cooking for about 1 minute and when golden underneath, scoop the quesadilla up on a large spatula and carefully turn it over.

5 Cook the other side for about 1 minute, or until golden and the cheese has melted. Place on a chopping board, then repeat with the remaining ingredients. Slice both into wedges. Serve hot.

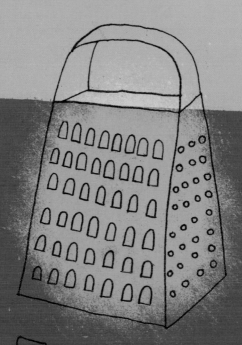

3 Heat the remaining oil in the frying pan, and then add one tortilla. Top with half the chicken mixture, leaving a little bit of room around the edges. Sprinkle over half the coriander and half the cheese.

Top Tip
Guacamole and tomato salsa (see pages 30–31) are both delicious with quesadillas. Either spread them on the tortilla in step 3, before you add the chicken, or just dollop on the top.

Samosas

These spicy savoury pastries are from India, where they are usually served with chutney. Traditionally, samosas are fried, but in this healthier recipe they are baked. You can buy filo pastry ready-made and frozen.

Top Tip
Take care when handling filo pastry; it's very easy to tear. It also dries out quickly. So, while you are preparing one samosa, keep the rest of the filo sheets covered with a damp tea towel or cling film.

MAKES 12 SAMOSAS
PREPARATION: 1 HOUR
COOKING: 20–25 MINUTES

4 potatoes, about 600 g
  (1 lb 5 oz), peeled and cut
  into large chunks
2 tbsp sunflower oil
1 tsp finely grated fresh ginger
1 garlic clove, finely chopped
1 onion, finely chopped
1 small carrot, peeled and
  finely chopped
100 g (3½ oz) frozen peas
1 tbsp garam masala
2 tsp cumin seeds
salt and freshly ground
  black pepper
2 tbsp chopped fresh coriander
6 sheets filo pastry

1 Cook the potatoes in boiling salted water for 20 minutes. Drain and cool, then cut into ½-cm (¼-in) pieces. Heat the oil in a frying pan and cook the ginger, garlic, onion, and carrot for about 3 minutes, stirring until softened.

2 To the pan, add the peas, garam masala, cumin seeds, and 1 tbsp water. Season with salt and pepper and stir well. Cook for about 2 minutes, then add the diced potatoes. Continue to cook for 2 minutes, then stir in the coriander. Set aside to cool.

3 Preheat the oven to 200°C (400°F/Gas 6). Unroll the filo pastry, peel off one sheet, lay it flat on a clean surface, and brush with melted butter. Cut the filo into strips roughly 12 x 40 cm (5 x 16 in).

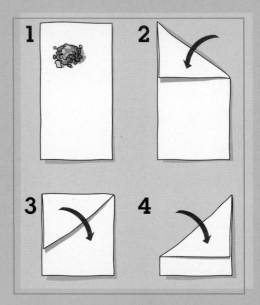

4 Place 1–2 tsp of the filling on one end of a strip (1). Fold a corner of the pastry over the filling to make a triangle (2). Fold down the triangle (3) and continue down the strip, alternating diagonal and straight folds, until you reach the bottom (4). Fold up any extra bits to give neat triangular parcels.

5 Place the samosas on a buttered baking tray, brush the tops with butter, and bake for 20–25 minutes, or until golden brown. Serve with an Indian chutney, such as mango or aubergine (brinjal), or with your own homemade tomato salsa or tzatziki (see pages 30–31).

To reheat the samosas, put them in the oven for about 10 minutes at 200°C (400°F/Gas 6), or pop them in a microwave on high for 1 minute.

Make some fresh mint raita (see page 45) to dip the samosas in.

If you like a bit of spice, serve up some aubergine (brinjal) chutney.

Meaty fillings

For a meat alternative, replace the potatoes with chicken or lamb mince. Put in about 300 g (10 oz) minced meat at the beginning of step 2 and stir well. Cook for 5 minutes, or until browned. Continue steps 2–5 in the same way.

For a quick dip, tomato sauce (ketchup) is always popular.

Bread snacks

When you need food in a hurry, you probably turn to bread for a quick sandwich fix, using the same old fillings. But bread doesn't have to be boring – here are a few ideas to liven things up. And if you are looking for an appetizer, or something to make a soup more substantial, flavour slices of bread with garlic, tomato, and fresh herbs.

Garlic bread (serves 4)

Preheat the oven to 200°C (400°F/Gas 6). Mix 100 g (3½ oz) butter with 3 finely chopped garlic cloves, 1 tbsp chopped fresh parsley, a squeeze of lemon juice, and some seasoning. Make cuts in a baguette, without cutting all the way through. Spread the garlic butter between the slices, then wrap in foil and bake 10 minutes.

If chopping garlic is a chore, use a crusher instead.

Crostini are a delicious appetizer.

Tomato and basil crostini (makes 12)

Cut a baguette into 12 thin slices and toast them on both sides under the grill. Mix 8 deseeded and chopped tomatoes with ½ a chopped red onion, a handful of chopped fresh basil leaves, 1 tsp balsamic vinegar and some salt. Rub each slice with a cut garlic clove, then spoon some tomato mixture on each one with a fresh basil leaf and some freshly ground black pepper. Drizzle over some olive oil before serving.

Croque monsieur (makes 4)

Make a cheesy sauce: melt 30 g (1 oz) butter in a saucepan, stir in 2 tbsp plain flour, cook for 1 minute, then remove from the heat and stir in 100 ml (3½ fl oz) milk until smooth. Beat in 75 g (2½ oz) grated Gruyère cheese, 2 tsp Dijon mustard, and 1 egg yolk. Toast 4 bread slices on one side and top each with 1 slice of ham and 1 slice of Gruyère cheese. Top with another slice of bread and spread each with a quarter of the sauce. Grill until golden.

Chicken club sandwich (makes 1)

Toast 3 slices of bread, and then spread the first slice with mayonnaise and some wholegrain mustard. Slice a small cooked, skinless chicken breast, and lay half of it, on the toast followed by 2 rashers of cooked streaky bacon. Add some sliced tomato and shredded lettuce. Top with the second slice of toast and repeat the layers. Top with the last slice of toast, secure the monster sandwich with 2 cocktail sticks pushed through a gherkin, cut diagonally, and enjoy!

Go veggie by swapping the chicken with slices of Leerdammer or mild Cheddar cheese and using watercress rather than lettuce.

Chicken Caesar wrap (makes 4)

In a blender, whizz 2 chopped anchovy fillets with 1 finely chopped garlic clove, a squeeze of lemon juice, 2 tsp Dijon mustard, and 4 tbsp mayonnaise. Slice 4 small roast chicken breasts and toss into the dressing. Divide the mixture between 4 soft wraps. Top with shredded lettuce, grated carrot, fresh grated Parmesan cheese, and freshly ground black pepper, and roll up.

For a veggie wrap, leave out the anchovies from the dressing, and fill the soft wraps with sliced avocado, cucumber sticks, and grilled red peppers. Top with lettuce, Parmesan cheese, and the dressing before rolling.

Cheese, ham, and chutney panini (makes 2)

Cut 2 panini or ciabatta rolls in half and fill each with 50 g (1¾ oz) thin sliced smoked ham, 1 tbsp chutney, and 1 slice of mild Cheddar or Emmental cheese. Brush the tops with olive oil, and cook on a hot griddle pan, pressing down well and turning until golden on both sides and the cheese is melted.

Toast the panini in a griddle pan – but if you don't have one, a regular frying pan is fine.

Big food

Everyone needs to eat one big meal a day to keep them going, so learn to cook what you like to eat – a warming stew, a big plate of pasta, or a spicy stir-fry. Be sure to make enough. Hungry people appear from nowhere when there are tempting smells and the sounds of activity from the kitchen!

Snip some spring onions and parsley on top for flavour and colour.

Pot of veg

For a vegetarian jambalaya, skip to step 2 and fry the ingredients in 1 tbsp sunflower oil. Add 1 diced sweet potato or butternut squash, 125 g (4½ oz) frozen peas, and 1 drained 400 g (14 oz) can of kidney beans. Follow the rest of the recipe opposite until the vegetables are cooked.

Jumbalaya

This colourful one-pot rice dish is full of the flavours of the Cajun cooking from Louisiana, USA. Its name literally means "jumbled" or "mixed up" because it is a mix of rice, meat, seafood, and vegetables.

SERVES 6
PREPARATION: 30 MINUTES
COOKING: 25 MINUTES

200 g (7 oz) chorizo or any other
  spicy sausage, sliced
2 skinless chicken breasts, cut
  into bite-sized pieces
1 onion, finely chopped
2 garlic cloves, finely chopped
1 red pepper, deseeded
  and chopped
2 celery sticks, diced
1 green chilli, deseeded and
  finely chopped
350 g (12 oz) long-grain rice
1 tsp chilli powder
2 tbsp tomato purée
2 tsp dried thyme
½ tsp paprika
salt and freshly ground
  black pepper
400 g (14 oz) can
  chopped tomatoes
900 ml (1½ pints)
  vegetable stock
200 g (7 oz) raw peeled prawns

1 In a large frying pan dry fry the chorizo for 2 minutes over a medium heat until it releases its lovely golden oil. Add the chicken and fry for 3–4 minutes until browned. Remove the chorizo and chicken and set aside.

3 Return the chorizo and chicken to the pan and add the thyme, and paprika, and season with salt and pepper. Pour in the tomatoes and the stock, stir, then bring to the boil.

4 Reduce the heat to low, cover tightly with a lid or foil, and simmer for 20 minutes, stirring occasionally. Stir in the prawns and cook for a further 5 minutes, or until the liquid has been absorbed, the rice is tender, and the prawns are pink.

2 Add the onion, garlic, pepper, celery, and green chilli to the pan and fry, stirring, for 5 minutes, or until softened. Add the rice, chilli powder, and tomato purée and cook for 2 minutes.

Leave the chilli seeds in if you like a bit of heat!

Chicken jalfrezi

Curry recipes can look a bit daunting, but don't be put off by the long list of ingredients – most are small quantities of spices. This dish is really simple to make and has a rich tomato sauce.

Top Tip
You can adjust the heat by varying the type of chilli you use. Smaller ones are usually hotter, but just use one large fat one if you prefer a milder curry.

SERVES 4
PREPARATION: 25 MINUTES
COOKING: 15 MINUTES

1 tbsp sunflower oil
2.5-cm (1-in) piece fresh
   ginger, peeled and
   finely chopped
3 garlic cloves, finely chopped
1 onion, sliced
2 tsp ground cumin
2 tsp black mustard seeds
1 tsp ground turmeric
2 tbsp masala curry paste
1 red pepper, deseeded
   and sliced
½ green pepper, deseeded
   and sliced
2 green chillies, deseeded
   and sliced
675 g (1½ lb) skinless
   chicken breast, diced
400 g (14 oz) can
   chopped tomatoes
3 tbsp chopped fresh coriander
salt and freshly ground
   black pepper

1 Heat the oil in a large saucepan over a medium heat. Add the ginger, garlic, and onion and fry until the onion starts to soften. Stir in the spices and curry paste and cook for a further 1–2 minutes.

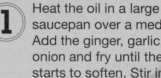

2 Add the peppers and chillies and fry for 5 minutes. Turn up the heat, add the chicken, and cook for 5 minutes, or until lightly browned.

3 Add the tomatoes and coriander. Season with salt and pepper, then reduce the heat and simmer for 15 minutes, or until the sauce has reduced slightly. Serve with plain rice or any of the side dishes on pages 44–45.

Chickpea curry

As with most spicy dishes, the flavours of this vegetarian curry are often better the next day, so look forward to any leftovers – if there are any!

Top Tip
You can swap the butternut squash with the same quantity of pumpkin, sweet potatoes, or even plain potatoes.

SERVES 4
PREPARATION: 15 MINUTES
COOKING: 20–25 MINUTES

2 tbsp sunflower oil

1 onion, finely chopped

2 garlic cloves, finely chopped

2.5-cm (1-in) piece fresh ginger, peeled and finely chopped

1 green chilli, deseeded and finely chopped

1 tsp ground cumin

1 tsp ground coriander

1 tsp ground turmeric

1 butternut squash, about 750 g (1 lb 10 oz), peeled, seeds scooped out, and diced

400 g (14 oz) can chopped tomatoes

400 g (14 oz) can coconut milk

400 g (14 oz) can chickpeas, drained

200 g (7 oz) fresh leaf spinach, chopped

handful of fresh coriander, chopped

half a lemon

1 Heat the oil in a large pan over a medium heat and fry the onion, garlic, ginger, and chilli with the spices for about 5 minutes, until the onion starts to soften. Add the butternut squash and mix with the ingredients in the pan.

3 Stir in the spinach, and when it has wilted, add the coriander and a squeeze of lemon juice. Serve with plain rice or any of the side dishes on pages 44–45.

2 Tip in the tomatoes, coconut milk, and chickpeas, and simmer for 15–20 minutes, or until the squash is tender when you pierce it with a fork.

Use reduced-fat coconut milk for a healthier version.

43

Curry feast

It's fun and traditional to serve Indian curries with a selection of sides, including breads, relishes, vegetables, and flavoured rice. Here are a few delicious dishes – pick one or two to eat with a curry, or make them all for a real Indian feast! All recipes serve 4–6.

Naan breads are great for mopping up curry sauces. Buy them from the supermarket and follow the instructions on the pack to heat them up in the oven.

Indian salad

Mix together 1 finely chopped red onion, 1 deseeded and finely chopped green chilli, 2 finely chopped tomatoes, finely chopped ¼ of a cucumber, a small handful of chopped fresh mint, and a handful of chopped fresh coriander. Season with salt and freshly ground black pepper, then cover and chill until ready to serve.

Top the daal with some extra fried onions and chillies.

Daal

Cook 1 chopped onion in 3 tbsp sunflower oil until soft. Stir in 1 cinnamon stick, a 3-cm (1¼-in) piece grated fresh ginger, 1 tsp each of ground turmeric, ground cumin, and ground coriander, and 200 g (7 oz) split red lentils. Add 750 ml (1¼ pints) vegetable stock and 1 bay leaf. Season, then simmer for 25–30 minutes, stirring frequently. Fry 3 sliced garlic cloves and 1 deseeded and chopped red chilli in 2 tbsp sunflower oil until golden. Stir into the lentils with 2 tbsp fresh lemon juice and serve.

Raita

Coarsely grate ½ a peeled and deseeded cucumber onto kitchen towel and squeeze out the excess water. Stir into 250 g (9 oz) plain yoghurt with a small handful of chopped fresh mint, a pinch of salt, and 1 tsp of sugar.

For a spicy kick, add ½ tsp ground cumin to the raita.

Poppadoms are thin, crispy flatbreads made from chickpea flour. Buy them already prepared, and dip them in chutney, raita, or top with Indian salad.

Stir in 85 g (3 oz) thawed frozen peas to the pilau for colour.

Spicy pilau rice

Heat 1 tbsp sunflower oil in a large saucepan. Add 1 small finely chopped onion, and fry until golden. Stir in 1 cinnamon stick, 1 tsp cumin seeds, 1 tsp black mustard seeds, 2 cardamom pods, 6 whole cloves, and 2 tsp ground turmeric, and cook for 1 minute. Add 300 g (10 oz) basmati rice and stir until coated. Pour in 600 ml (1 pint) boiling water and some salt, then bring to the boil. Cover, then gently simmer for 12–15 minutes, until all the water has been absorbed.

Couscous is made from wheat flour that is mixed with water and rolled into grains.

Moreish Moorish veg

It's easy to adapt this recipe to make a vegetarian tagine. In the oil, with the onion and garlic, fry 1 small diced sweet potato, 1 quartered head of fennel, 8 halved new potatoes, 1 coarsely chopped red pepper, and chunks of 1 small aubergine and 2 courgettes. Cook for 5 minutes. Stir in the spices, vegetable stock, and tomatoes and cook for 1 hour. Stir in the rest of the ingredients with a 400 g (14 oz) can chickpeas and cook for a further 20 minutes.

Lumb tagine

This North African dish is named after the special dome-shaped pot it is traditionally cooked in, but it works just as well in a normal casserole. It's usually served with couscous, but if you don't have any, use rice instead.

SERVES 4
PREPARATION: 20 MINUTES
COOKING: 2 HOURS
  20 MINUTES

2 tbsp sunflower oil

450 g (1 lb) lean lamb, cut into
  5-cm (2-in) pieces

1 onion, finely chopped

1 garlic clove, finely chopped

2.5-cm (1-in) piece fresh
  ginger, peeled and grated

1 tsp ground cinnamon

1 tsp ground cumin

1 tsp ground coriander

salt and freshly ground
  black pepper

300 ml (10 fl oz) lamb or
  vegetable stock

4 tomatoes, quartered

100 g (3½ oz) dried apricots or
  pitted prunes, halved

60 g (2 oz) whole
  blanched almonds

½ lemon, juice only

1 tbsp clear honey

For the couscous
250 g (9 oz) couscous
2 tbsp olive oil

Top Tip
The meat should be so tender that it falls apart. If it is still a little tough after step 2, simmer for an extra 20 minutes before adding the dried fruits.

1 Heat the oil in a heavy flameproof casserole and lightly brown the lamb on all sides. Stir in the onion, garlic, ginger, and spices and cook for another 2 minutes.

3 Add the apricots or prunes, almonds, lemon juice, and honey. Bring to the boil, then reduce the heat and simmer for a further 20 minutes, adding extra stock if the sauce becomes too thick.

2 Season with salt and pepper, then add the stock and tomatoes. Bring to the boil, then reduce the heat to low. Cover the pan and simmer for 1¾–2 hours, stirring every 30 minutes, or until the meat is really tender.

4 Place the couscous in a large bowl and pour over 300 ml (10 fl oz) boiling water. Stir, cover with cling film, and leave to stand for 5 minutes.

5 Fluff up the couscous grains with a fork, then drizzle over the olive oil and gently mix through. Serve with the tagine.

Chilli con carne

This is a great dish to feed a crowd, and you cook it in one big pot. Make the chilli the day before you need it – the flavours will improve overnight – so all that's left to do is heat it through and cook up the rice.

SERVES 4
PREPARATION: 25 MINUTES
COOKING: 45 MINUTES

3 tbsp olive oil
2 onions, chopped
3 garlic cloves, finely chopped
2 green chillies, finely
  chopped, or 2 tsp dried
  chilli flakes
1 red pepper, deseeded
  and diced
1 tsp ground cumin
2 tsp paprika
1 tsp dried oregano
500 g (1 lb 2 oz) beef mince
2 tbsp tomato purée
400 g (14 oz) can red
  kidney beans, drained
  and rinsed
2 bay leaves
400 g (14 oz) can
  chopped tomatoes
500 ml (16 fl oz) beef stock
salt and freshly ground
  black pepper
small bunch fresh
  coriander, chopped

To serve
soured cream
1 lime, cut into wedges

1 Heat the olive oil in a large heavy pan and gently fry the onions, garlic, and chillies for 5 minutes until softened. Add the red pepper, spices, and oregano and cook for another 2 minutes.

2 Turn the heat up to high, add the beef mince, and cook, breaking it up with a wooden spoon for 3–4 minutes until browned. Add the tomato purée and cook for another 2 minutes.

3 Add the kidney beans, bay leaves, tomatoes, and just enough stock to cover. Stir well, season with salt and pepper, and bring to the boil. Reduce the heat, cover, and simmer for 45 minutes, stirring occasionally.

4 Stir through the chopped coriander and spoon the chilli over cooked rice. Serve with the lime wedges, to squeeze over the chilli, and soured cream to tone down the heat.

Look out for jalapeño chillies – they have a fragrant flavour and are not too hot!

48

Top Tip

If there's any chilli left over, use it to make burritos. Just heat up the meat and spoon it on to tortilla wraps with guacamole, soured cream, and some grated cheese. Roll them up and enjoy!

For a bit of crunch, scoop up the chilli with tortilla chips.

Chilli... without carne

Chilli con carne is Spanish for "chilli with meat", but don't let this stop you making a vegetarian version. Replace the meat with 1 deseeded, finely chopped green pepper and add an extra 400 g (14 oz) can of different beans in step 3. There are lots of different types – black-eyed beans, butter beans, borlotti beans, or even chickpeas. Use vegetable stock instead of beef.

Guacamole (see page 30) is great with chilli con carne.

Top Tip

To make breadcrumbs, tear stale bread into pieces and whizz them up in a food processor, or rub thick slices against the large holes of a cheese grater.

Garnish the dish with some chopped fresh parsley.

Tapas feast

Tapas is the name for a light meal made up of lots of small dishes that you dip into. Make your own tapas spread by serving the meatballs with other dishes like Spanish omelette (see pages 20–21), empanadas (pages 98–99), fried chorizo sausage, sliced Manchego cheese, and lots of bread.

Spanish meatballs

Meatballs are popular all over the world, and each country has its own special recipe. They can be fried, steamed, served in a soup, or even stuffed with cheese. These spicy meatballs in tomato sauce are found in Spain and Latin America.

SERVES 6
PREPARATION: 30 MINUTES
COOKING: 25 MINUTES

2 onions, finely chopped
250 g (9 oz) pork mince
250 g (9 oz) beef mince
1 tsp dried oregano
60 g (2 oz) fresh white
  breadcrumbs
1 tsp ground cumin
½ tsp grated nutmeg
1 egg, beaten
salt and freshly ground
  black pepper
5 tbsp olive oil
2 garlic cloves, finely chopped
pinch of chilli powder
2 x 400 g (14 oz) cans
  chopped tomatoes
100 ml (3½ fl oz)
  vegetable stock

1 Place half of the onions, the pork and beef mince, oregano, breadcrumbs, cumin, nutmeg, and egg into a large bowl. Mix well, and then season with salt and freshly ground black pepper.

2 Using slightly damp hands, roll the mince mixture into meatballs about 5 cm (2 in) across.

3 Heat 3 tbsp of the olive oil in a frying pan and gently fry the meatballs for 5–6 minutes, turning regularly, until completely browned. Remove from the pan and set aside.

4 To make the sauce, heat the rest of the olive oil in the pan over a medium heat, and gently fry the remaining onions, the garlic, and chilli powder until soft and golden.

5 Add the chopped tomatoes, season with salt and pepper, and cook for 5–6 minutes.

6 Add the stock to the sauce and stir well, then drop in the meatballs. Simmer for 25 minutes, or until the sauce is lovely and thick and the meatballs are cooked through. Serve with rice or crusty bread to soak up the rich tomato sauce.

Chicken paprikash

This stew is a Hungarian recipe and a great winter warmer. The simple ingredients are transformed by the spice paprika, made from dried sweet peppers, which gives the dish its wonderful flavour and colour.

SERVES 4
PREPARATION: 20 MINUTES
COOKING: 45–55 MINUTES

8 boneless chicken thighs
salt and freshly ground
  black pepper
2 tbsp olive oil
2 red onions, chopped
2 garlic cloves, finely chopped
2 tbsp sweet paprika
¼ tsp caraway seeds
250 ml (8 fl oz) chicken stock
1 tbsp red wine vinegar
1 tbsp tomato purée
1 tsp sugar
2 red peppers, sliced
250 g (9 oz) cherry tomatoes
1 small handful fresh parsley,
  finely chopped
150 ml (5 fl oz) soured cream

 Season the chicken with salt and freshly ground black pepper. Heat 1 tbsp of the oil in a large flameproof casserole over a medium heat, and brown the chicken for 5 minutes. Transfer to a large plate and set aside.

 Heat the rest of the oil in the pan and fry the onions and garlic for about 5 minutes, or until the onions have softened. Stir in the paprika and caraway seeds, then return the chicken to the casserole.

 Mix together the stock, vinegar, tomato purée, and sugar. Pour over the chicken and bring to the boil. Season, then reduce to a low heat, cover, and simmer for 30–40 minutes, or until the chicken is tender.

 Add the peppers and cherry tomatoes, and stir to mix everything together. Cover and simmer for a further 15 minutes.

5 Remove from the heat and top with the parsley and spoonfuls of soured cream. Serve with some cooked rice, potatoes, or buttered noodles.

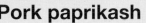

Pork paprikash

This recipe is also good with pork. Cut 450 g
(1 lb) pork tenderloin into 2.5 cm (1 in) cubes
and brown as you would the chicken thighs.
Proceed as in the original recipe, but in
step 3, simmer the stew for just 20 minutes.
Add the peppers and tomatoes as in step 4,
then cook for a further 10 minutes before
adding the parsley and soured cream.

Top Tip
If you don't have
fresh tomatoes,
you can use a
400 g (14 oz) can
of chopped
tomatoes instead.

Fishcakes

Crispy on the outside but soft on the inside, these salmon fishcakes are a real treat. Prepare them ahead of time, keep them in the fridge, then cook them up when you're ready to eat. Serve with a simple green salad.

MAKES 8 FISHCAKES
PREPARATION: 45 MINUTES,
** PLUS CHILLING**
COOKING: 6–8 MINUTES

600 g (1 lb 5 oz) potatoes, peeled
  and cut into large chunks
salt and freshly ground
  black pepper
450 g (1 lb) salmon fillets
milk, to cover fish
1 bay leaf
1 lemon, 1 strip of zest
  (use a vegetable peeler for
  this), and wedges to serve
3 tbsp fresh chopped parsley
4 spring onions, chopped
200 g (7 oz) day-old white bread,
  crusts removed
4 tbsp plain flour, plus extra
  for dusting
1 large egg, beaten
2 tbsp olive oil

Instead of fresh salmon,
you can use the same
quantity of smoked
haddock, or tinned
salmon or tuna.

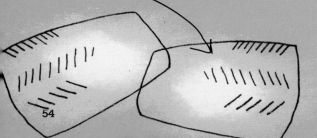

1 Cook the potatoes in boiling salted water for 20 minutes, or until tender when pierced with a knife. Drain in a colander, then tip back into the pan.

2 Meanwhile, place the salmon in a small pan with enough milk to cover. Add the bay leaf and strip of lemon zest, place the pan over a medium heat, and let the milk come slowly to the boil. Cook for 1 minute, then cover with a lid and turn off the heat. Set aside to cool. The fish should now look pink.

3 Mash the potatoes with a masher or fork, adding 2 tbsp of the milk in which the fish was poached. Lift the fish out of the milk, remove any skin and bones, and flake into a large bowl.

4 Add the mashed potatoes, parsley, spring onions, and plenty of salt and freshly ground pepper. Finely grate over the remaining lemon zest and mix everything together well.

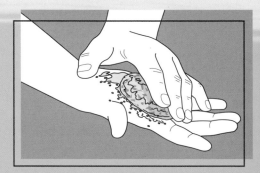

5 Divide the mixture into 8 and shape each one into a 2-cm (¾-in) thick cake using a little flour to stop it sticking to your hands. Place on a plate and pop them in the fridge to firm up for 30 minutes.

6 Put the bread into a blender or food processor, and whizz until it forms crumbs, then tip on to a plate. Tip the egg on to another plate and the flour on to another.

7 Coat all the cakes in the flour, then the egg, and then the crumbs. Keep in the refrigerator until ready to cook.

8 Heat the olive oil in a large frying pan. Add the fishcakes and cook for 3–4 minutes on both sides until golden. If you can't fit them all in the pan together, keep the first batch hot in the oven while cooking the rest. Serve with the lemon wedges to squeeze over and a green salad.

Top Tip

If you don't want to fry the fishcakes, put them in the oven at 220 °C (425 °F/Gas 7) for 15 minutes, then to crisp them up, put them under a hot grill until golden, turning once.

Pad Thai

Served from food carts all around Thailand, Pad Thai is the ultimate street food. Some of the ingredients sound unusual, but you should be able to find them in large supermarkets.

SERVES 4
PREPARATION: 15 MINUTES
COOKING: 5–6 MINUTES

350 g (12 oz) flat rice noodles
2 tbsp fresh chopped coriander
1 red chilli, deseeded and
  finely chopped
1 garlic clove, finely chopped
4 tbsp sunflower oil
250 g (9 oz) uncooked
  shelled prawns
5 shallots, finely chopped
2 eggs, beaten
1 tbsp light brown sugar
1 tbsp oyster sauce
1 tbsp fish sauce
juice of 1 lime
2 tbsp sweet chilli sauce
250 g (9 oz) fresh bean sprouts
4 spring onions, sliced
1 lime, cut into wedges, to serve

1 Prepare the noodles according to the instructions on the pack and set aside. Mix together the coriander, chilli, and garlic with the oil in a small bowl.

2 Heat half the oil mixture in a wok. When very hot, add the prawns and stir-fry for 1 minute until pink, then remove from the pan and set aside.

3 Add the remaining oil mixture and fry the shallots for 1 minute. Add the eggs and sugar, and cook for 1 minute, stirring to scramble the eggs.

4 Stir in the oyster sauce, fish sauce, lime juice, sweet chilli sauce, cooked rice noodles, and bean sprouts and stir-fry for 2 minutes.

5 Return the prawns to the wok with the spring onions and mix together for 1–2 minutes, or until everything is piping hot. Serve with the lime wedges on the side.

Chinese pork stir-fry

For the perfect stir-fry, cut the ingredients into equal-sized pieces, so they take the same time to cook, get the wok hot, and keep the food moving by constantly stirring it.

SERVES 4
PREPARATION: 15 MINUTES,
PLUS 15 MINUTES
MARINATING
COOKING: 6–7 MINUTES

400 g (14 oz) pork tenderloin, finely sliced
1 tbsp Chinese rice vinegar
1 tbsp soy sauce
2 tsp sesame oil
1 tsp cornflour
200 g (7 oz) pak choi
2.5-cm (1-in) piece fresh ginger, peeled and grated
1 garlic clove, finely sliced
2 tbsp sunflower oil
3 tbsp oyster sauce

 1 Place the pork in a bowl with the rice vinegar, soy sauce, sesame oil, and cornflour. Stir to completely coat the meat, then set aside to marinate for 15 minutes.

 2 Meanwhile, cut the leaves off the pak choi and set aside. Chop the stalks into 2-cm (¾-in) slices.

3 Heat the sunflower oil in a wok until very hot and slightly smoking. Add the pork mixture and stir-fry for 2–3 minutes, or until brown, then remove to a plate.

4 Add the ginger and garlic to the wok and stir-fry for 1–2 minutes, or until golden. Add the pak choi stalks and stir-fry for 2 minutes, then add the leaves, oyster sauce, and 3–4 tbsp water and continue cooking until the sauce starts bubbling.

5 Return the pork to the wok and heat through for 1–2 minutes. Serve with boiled rice.

If you can't find pak choi, use cabbage or broccoli.

57

Cannelloni

This is a vegetarian dish made of large tubes of pasta filled with spinach and ricotta – a light curd cheese from Italy. Traditionally, cannelloni is topped with a white sauce. This recipe uses crème fraîche instead, as a shortcut.

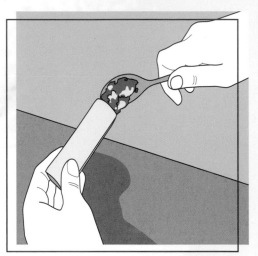

Top Tip
You can use cooked lasagne sheets instead of cannelloni tubes. Just dollop some of the mixture in the middle of each sheet, then roll up into tube shapes.

SERVES 4
PREPARATION: 35 MINUTES
COOKING: 45–55 MINUTES

knob of butter
olive oil
2 garlic cloves, finely sliced
500 g (1 lb 2 oz) fresh spinach
　leaves, washed
300 g (11 oz) ricotta cheese
1 egg, beaten
60 g (2 oz) freshly grated
　Parmesan cheese
¼ tsp grated nutmeg
salt and freshly ground
　black pepper
16 cannelloni tubes
2 x 400 g (14 oz) cans
　chopped tomatoes
pinch of sugar
handful of fresh basil
　leaves, torn
500 ml (16 fl oz)
　crème fraîche
2 tbsp water
200 g (7 oz) mozzarella cheese,
　torn into pieces

1 Preheat the oven to 180°C (350°F/Gas 4). Heat the butter and a drizzle of olive oil in a large saucepan and fry one of the sliced garlic cloves until soft. Stir in the spinach, a handful at a time, until it has all wilted. Take the pan off the heat.

2 When cool, drain the spinach in a sieve, squeezing well to remove any excess water. Chop finely then place in a bowl and mix in the ricotta, beaten egg, and half the Parmesan cheese. Season with the grated nutmeg, salt, and freshly ground black pepper.

3 Use a teaspoon to scoop the ricotta mixture into the cannelloni tubes so each one is completely filled up. Lay the tubes close together in a lightly oiled baking dish.

4 Place the saucepan back on the heat, and soften the rest of the garlic in a little olive oil. Tip in the tomatoes and bring to the boil. Add the sugar and season with salt and freshly ground black pepper, then reduce the heat and simmer for 15 minutes, or until the sauce has thickened. Stir in the basil leaves, then pour the sauce over the cannelloni.

When ready, the top of the cannelloni should be golden and bubbling.

5 In a bowl, mix together the crème fraîche, the rest of the Parmesan cheese, some salt and freshly ground black pepper, and the water. Spoon the sauce over the tomato layer, top with the mozzarella cheese, then bake in the oven for 30–40 minutes.

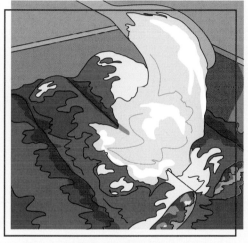

Cannelloni for carnivores

For meaty cannelloni, fill the pasta tubes with the Bolognese sauce from page 61. Top with the tomato sauce, crème fraîche, mozzarella, and a handful of Parmesan, and bake as above.

Pasta sauces

There is an amazing array of pasta shapes and sauces to try. Don't buy a sauce in jar, make your own! The flavours will taste so much fresher. These classic recipes are quick and easy, so you can use them again and again. All recipes serve 4.

spaghetti

penne

farfalle

Pasta shapes usually go with chunky sauces, and spaghetti and tagliatelle are best with thin sauces.

Tomato sauce
Fry 2 finely chopped garlic cloves and 1 chopped onion in a little olive oil. Stir in a 400 g (14 oz) can of chopped tomatoes, 1 tbsp tomato purée, and a pinch of sugar. Bring to the boil, then reduce the heat and simmer for 25 minutes, or until the sauce has thickened. Add a handful of torn fresh basil and season with salt and freshly ground black pepper. Cook 300 g (10 oz) dried pasta shapes and serve topped with the sauce.

Use low-fat cream and replace the bacon with lean ham for a healthier carbonara.

Spaghetti carbonara
Fry 6 chopped rashers of bacon and 1 finely chopped garlic clove in a little olive oil. Beat together 4 egg yolks, 150 ml (5 fl oz) single cream, 60 g (2 oz) grated Parmesan cheese, and plenty of freshly ground black pepper. Cook 400 g (14 oz) dried spaghetti. Drain, then return to the pan and toss with the bacon and egg mixture until the pasta is evenly coated.

Pesto

Toast 3 tbsp pine nuts in a dry frying pan, stirring until golden. Set aside. Put 125 g (4½ oz) fresh basil, 2 finely chopped garlic cloves, 90 ml (3 fl oz) olive oil, and the cooled pine nuts in a food processor and pulse until blended to a coarse purée. Add 50 g (1¾ oz) finely grated Parmesan cheese and blend again. Cook 400 g (14 oz) dried pasta. Drain, then return to the pan and stir in the pesto.

To bulk up pasta with pesto, add cooked vegetable, such as broccoli or mushrooms.

Pasta puttanesca

Fry 1 chopped onion and 1 finely chopped garlic clove in a little olive oil until soft. Add 1 deseeded and chopped red chilli, 50 g (1¾ oz) drained tin anchovies, 175 g (6 oz) chopped black olives, 1 tbsp capers, and a 400 g (14 oz) can chopped tomatoes. Bring to the boil and simmer for 20 minutes, or until thickened. Cook 400 g (14 oz) dried pasta and toss through the sauce.

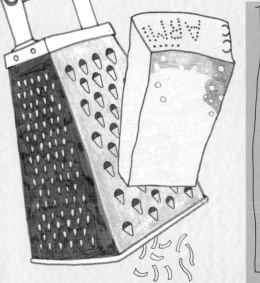

Bolognese sauce

Fry 2 finely chopped garlic cloves, 1 chopped onion, 2 chopped celery sticks, and 1 grated carrot in a little olive oil for 5 minutes. Tip in 500 g (1 lb 2 oz) of beef mince and cook, stirring, until browned. Add a 400 g (14 oz) can chopped tomatoes, 2 tbsp tomato purée, 300 ml (10 fl oz) water, a beef stock cube, and 1 tsp dried oregano. Season with salt and freshly ground black pepper, then simmer for 45 minutes. Cook 400 g (14 oz) dried spaghetti and serve topped with the sauce.

Lumb kebabs

These tasty kebabs are fantastic on the barbeque, but if it rains, just cook them under the grill inside. You can use cubes of chicken or fish instead of lamb if you prefer.

Top Tip
For really flavoursome and tender kebabs, prepare them the day before and leave the meat to marinate overnight.

SERVES 4
PREPARATION: 20 MINUTES,
  PLUS MARINATING
COOKING: 12–14 MINUTES

For the marinade
2 garlic cloves, finely chopped
1 tsp chilli flakes or powder
1 tsp ground cumin
1 tsp ground cinnamon
1 tsp ground coriander
1 tbsp clear runny honey
handful of fresh mint leaves,
  finely chopped
1 tbsp olive oil
juice of ½ lemon

For the kebabs
500 g (1 lb 2 oz) lamb neck
  fillet, cut into 4 cm
  (1½ in) cubes
1 red pepper, deseeded and
  cut into bite-sized chunks
1 red onion, cut into
  bite-sized chunks

1 Mix all the marinade ingredients together in a non-metallic bowl. Add the lamb and toss gently to completely coat the meat. Cover and refrigerate for at least 2 hours.

2 Meanwhile, soak 4 wooden skewers in water to prevent them from catching alight during grilling. Or you can use metal ones if you have them.

3 Thread the cubes of lamb onto the skewers, alternating with pieces of pepper and onion. Preheat the grill or get the barbecue hot.

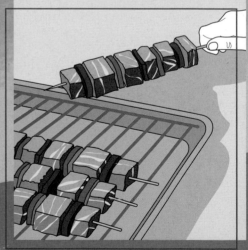

4 Grill the kebabs for 12–14 minutes, turning every few minutes. The meat should be brown on the outside, but still pink and juicy inside. Slide the meat and veg off the skewers with a fork, then stuff them in pitta breads or serve with a salad or rice.

Scatter with fresh mint and sliced chillies before serving for extra colour, flavour, and spice.

Minus the meat

For a vegetarian alternative, replace the meat with pieces of cubed aubergine and courgette, halloumi cheese, or all three.

Barbecue food

Here are some great recipes for the grill. When cooking on coals, getting the timing right can be tricky, so if you're entertaining, make sure you've got lots of other food that doesn't need cooking, such as salads (see pages 18–19), dips (pages 30–31), and garlic bread (page 36).

BBQ ribs (serves 4)
Simmer 1 kg (2¼ lb) pork spare ribs in salted water for 30 minutes, then drain, rinse, and leave to cool. In a saucepan, bring to the boil 8 tbsp tomato ketchup, 1 tbsp brown sugar, 2 tbsp Worcester sauce, 1 tbsp cider vinegar, 2 tsp mustard, ½ tsp smoked paprika, and 1 clove finely chopped garlic and simmer for 5 minutes. When cooled, brush all over the ribs and grill for 8–10 minutes, turning and coating with sauce regularly.

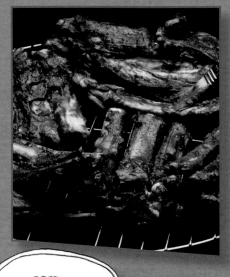

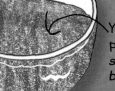

You can pour BBQ sauce on to burgers, too.

Best burgers (makes 4)
Fry ½ a finely chopped red onion and 2 finely chopped garlic cloves in 1 tbsp olive oil until soft, then leave to cool. Mix the onion into 500 g (1 lb 2 oz) minced beef with 1 tsp dried chilli flakes, a large pinch of salt, and freshly ground black pepper. Shape into 4 burgers and grill for about 6–8 minutes, turning once. Top each with a slice of cheese and, when it starts to melt, serve in a warm roll.

For extra flavour, add fresh chopped herbs such as parsley, thyme, or basil to the burger mix.

Put thin strips of vegetables, such as carrots and courgettes, inside your fish parcels for a meal in one.

Fish foil parcels
To barbecue salmon fillets, put each one in a foil parcel with sprigs of thyme or tarragon, orange zest, slices of lemon, and salt and pepper. Seal and grill for 4–5 minutes. You can also cook whole fish in foil. For sardines, mackerel, or sea bream up to 250 g (9 oz), add a squeeze of lime juice and ¼ tsp each of grated fresh ginger, chopped garlic, and chopped red chilli. Grill for 6–8 minutes. Test the fish is cooked with a knife – the meat should flake away easily.

Prawn skewers with peanut dip (serves 4)

Mix 1 tbsp olive oil with 2 finely chopped garlic cloves, the juice of ½ a lime, and 1 tbsp soy sauce. Add 450 g (1 lb) raw shelled prawns and marinate in the fridge for 15 minutes. Meanwhile, make the dip. Whisk 5 tbsp smooth peanut butter with 90 ml (3 fl oz) boiling water, 1 finely chopped garlic clove, 2 tbsp lime juice, 2 tbsp soy sauce, 1 tbsp sweet chilli sauce, and a pinch of salt and pepper. Thread the prawns on to skewers and grill for 2–3 minutes on each side.

Grilled aubergines (serves 2)

Combine 2 tbsp honey, 3 tbsp olive oil, 2 tsp cider vinegar, 2 tsp Dijon mustard, and 2 bruised and halved garlic cloves with 1 tbsp fresh oregano. Cut 2 small aubergines in half lengthways and rub the marinade over well. Season with salt and freshly ground black pepper, then grill for 8–10 minutes until tender. Serve with fresh tomato salsa (see page 31).

Caramelized fruit (serves 4)

Mix 3 tbsp honey with 1 tbsp lemon juice, 2 tbsp melted butter, and 1 tsp ground cinnamon. Thread thick slices of fresh fruit onto soaked wooden skewers – pineapple, apples, peaches, and pears are all delicious – and brush with the glaze. On a clean area of the grill, barbecue for 2–3 minutes on each side until golden.

The hot fruit is delicious with cold ice cream.

Something sweet

The finishing touch to a great meal is something sweet – for many it's the best bit! It's fun to make a spectacular dessert for a special occasion – perhaps something chocolatey, or a creamy cheesecake. But for everyday meals, there are lots of quick tricks for turning simple ingredients, such as fruit or ice cream, into delicious desserts.

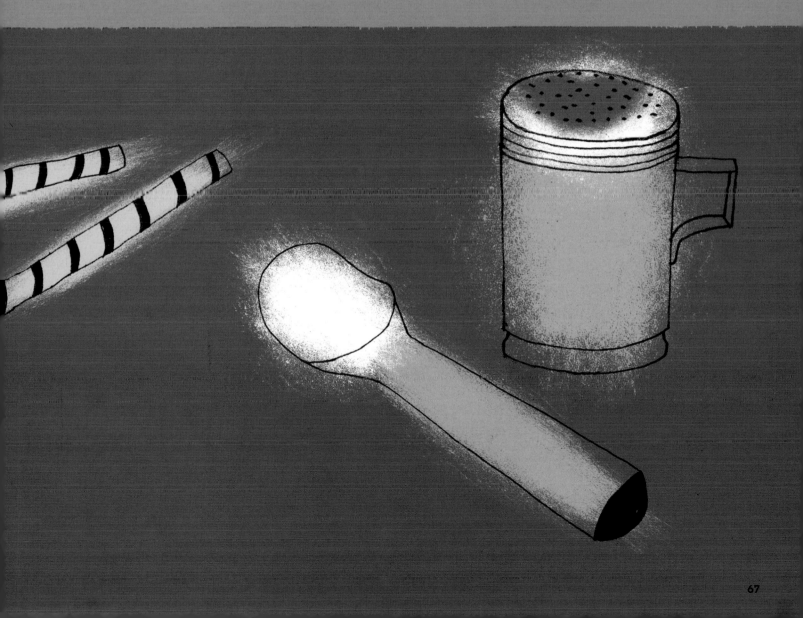

Fruit meringue

If you want a spectacular dessert, meringue never fails to impress. This mixture of fruit, cream, and crunchy meringue is irresistible, and is great for a party because you can make it ahead of time and then assemble it at the last minute.

SERVES 8
PREPARATION: 30 MINUTES
COOKING: 1¼–1¾ HOURS

4 egg whites
225 g (8 oz) caster sugar
600 ml (1 pint) double cream
2 kiwi fruits, peeled and sliced
450 g (1 lb) fresh strawberries
4 passion fruits

For a lower-fat filling, mix 250 ml (8 fl oz) fromage frais with 250 ml (8 fl oz) half-fat crème fraîche.

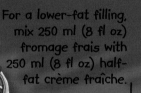

1 Heat the oven to 150°C (300°F/ Gas 2). Line a large baking tray with baking parchment and, using a dinner plate as a guide, draw a large circle on it.

2 Put the egg whites in a very clean large mixing bowl – they're going to increase dramatically in volume. Whisk until they form soft peaks.

3 Add a spoonful of sugar, and whisk for 1 minute. Continue adding sugar and then whisking until all the sugar is used up and the mixture is smooth. The meringue should stand in stiff peaks when you lift out the whisk.

4 Spoon the mixture into the circle on the baking parchment and push it out to the edge. Slightly hollow out the centre. Bake for 15 minutes, then lower the temperature to 140°C (275°F/Gas 1) and continue to cook for a further 1–1½ hours, or until crisp. Leave to cool.

5 Assemble the dessert no more than 2 hours before you're going to eat it. Whip the cream to form soft peaks, then spread it over the meringue. Arrange the fruit on top, scoop the passion-fruit seeds, scatter them over the fruit, and serve.

Put any fresh fruits that you like on top – raspberries, blueberries, or peaches.

You can make the meringue base ahead of time and keep it in an airtight tin for up to a week.

If you'd rather make lots of small meringues, just scoop dessert-spoonfuls of the mixture onto a lined baking tray and cook for 1–1½ hours. When cool, sandwich two together with whipped cream.

It's a mess!

A great way to use shop-bought meringues, or broken homemade ones, is to make what's officially called a "mess". Break into chunks and mix with lightly whipped cream and fruit that has been cut into small pieces or mashed. Dollop into glasses and eat straightaway.

69

Fruit feast

Fruit is delicious, nutritious, and versatile, so you don't have to do much to turn it into something special. Always use fruit that is ripe, it will be sweeter and have much more flavour. Feel free to adapt the recipes below to use your favourite fruits or what is in season.

Chocolate fruit

Melt 300 g (10 oz) chocolate chips and 3 tbsp double cream ina bowl set over a pan of simmering water. Stir until smooth, then spoon the chocolate sauce into small bowls. Serve with strawberries, or any fruit that you'd like to dip in.

Strawberry lollies (makes 6)

Wash and hull 200 g (7 oz) strawberries, then put them in a food processor with 2 tbsp icing sugar. Pulse, then sieve the purée into a bowl and discard the seeds. Mix the strawberry purée with 400 g (14 oz) plain yoghurt and add extra icing sugar to taste. Pour the mixture into 6 lollipop moulds and freeze for about 3 hours, or until frozen.

Fruit kebabs (makes 6)

It's fun to present fruit on skewers. Peel and slice into chunks 2 kiwi fruit and 2 small bananas, and slice 12 large strawberries in half. Thread the fruit on to 6 wooden skewers, then brush them with orange juice mixed with a little honey. This will prevent fruits like banana and apple from going brown. You can use any fruits, so mix and match your favourites – pineapple, peach, and melon all work well.

Fruit salad (serves 6)

Fruit salads work with all kinds of fruit combinations, but this one is a sure-fire winner. Remove the hulls and halve 250 g (9 oz) strawberries and place in a large bowl. Cut ½ a honeydew melon and ½ a cantaloupe into bite-sized chunks and add them to the bowl with a peeled and segmented orange, 125 g (4½ oz) raspberries, and 250 g (9 oz) seedless black grapes. Sprinkle over a little caster sugar, then chill until you are ready to eat.

Banana is brilliant baked with chocolate. Make a cut in the fruit lengthways, press in chunks of chocolate, wrap in foil, and bake for 20 minutes in a preheated oven set at 180°C (350°F/Gas 4).

Grilled peaches (serves 4)

Cut 4 ripe peaches in half and remove their stones. Mix together 2 tbsp soft light brown sugar with ¼ tsp ground cinnamon, scatter over the peaches, and place under a grill. Cook for about 5 minutes, or until they are golden and bubbling on top. Serve with a dollop of Greek yoghurt with some maple syrup, and pecan nuts scattered over.

71

Strawberry fool

This combination of fresh fruit and cream is an easy way to prepare a delicious dessert. This no-cook recipe has few ingredients, so you can make it when you are in a hurry.

SERVES 4
PREPARATION: 15 MINUTES,
  PLUS CHILLING

250 g (9 oz) strawberries, hulled
2 tbsp icing sugar
1 tbsp lemon juice
300 ml (10 fl oz) double cream
2 amaretti biscuits, crushed

1 Use a fork or potato masher to mash the strawberries, icing sugar, and lemon juice until soft and pulpy.

2 Whip the cream until soft peaks form, then fold the mashed fruit into the cream until it is marbled throughout.

3 Divide the mixture into 4 glasses, then chill in the refrigerator for 1–2 hours.

4 Once chilled, sprinkle the amaretti crumbs over the top and serve.

For a pretty finishing touch, decorate with a sprig of fresh mint.

For a smoother fool, whizz the fruit in a blender before adding to the cream.

Chocolate mousse

This classic French recipe is delicious but very rich, so serve it up in small portions. Note that the dessert contains raw eggs, and should not be eaten by very young children or the elderly (see page 8).

SERVES 6
PREPARATION: 20 MINUTES,
** PLUS CHILLING**

200 g (7 oz) dark chocolate,
  broken into pieces
45 g (1½ oz) butter
3 eggs, separated
45 g (1½ oz) caster sugar

1 Place the chocolate in a heatproof bowl over a pan of simmering water. When the chocolate has melted, add the butter and stir until smooth. Remove from the heat, and allow to cool slightly.

2 Beat the egg yolks into the mixture one at a time.

3 Whisk the eggs whites until they form stiff peaks, then whisk in the caster sugar. Stir some of the egg whites into the chocolate mixture, and gently fold in the rest.

4 Spoon into small pots or cups and chill for at least 2 hours.

Top Tip
It is a good idea to chill the chocolate mousse for about 2 hours before serving. This allows the chocolate to set and gives it a rich and velvety texture.

Use chocolate flavoured with mint to give the mousse a new twist.

If you like, top with fresh raspberries.

Stir 2 crumbled choc-chip cookies through the ice cream at the end of step 5, and you'll have choc-chip cookie ice cream!

Very berry nice
To add a ripple of fruit, mash 225 g (8 oz) strawberries or raspberries with 2 tbsp icing sugar. Press them through a sieve to remove the seeds, then stir the purée gently through the vanilla ice cream after you have whisked it for the last time at end of step 5.

Vanilla ice cream

Sweet, creamy, and deliciously cold, ice cream is always a treat, but homemade ice cream is even better, so learn to make your own – it's not difficult and you don't need an ice cream maker. This recipe uses an electric hand whisk instead.

SERVES 6
PREPARATION: 20 MINUTES,
PLUS FREEZING

½ **vanilla pod**
150 ml (5 fl oz) **full-fat milk**
2 **egg yolks**
4 tbsp **caster sugar**
300 ml (½ pint) **double cream**

To split a vanilla pod, score down it lengthways with a small sharp knife.

1 Split the vanilla pod, scrape out the seeds, then put the pod and seeds into a pan with the milk and heat to simmering point. Take off the heat and remove the pod. In a separate bowl, whisk the egg yolks and sugar together until pale, then pour in the milk and whisk again.

2 Return the mixture to a clean, pan and cook over a low heat, stirring constantly, until it thickens to the consistency of thick cream and coats the back of the wooden spoon. Don't be impatient and turn up the heat, or the mixture will curdle.

3 Cover the surface of the custard with cling film, to stop a skin forming, and set aside to cool.

4 Pour the double cream into a bowl and whisk until it forms soft peaks. Fold into the cold custard and pour into a freezer container.

5 Freeze for 2 hours, or until half frozen. Whisk with an electric hand whisk to break up the ice crystals. Half-freeze and whisk twice more, then leave to freeze completely.

Top Tip
Homemade ice cream freezes much harder than shop bought, so leave it to soften in the fridge for 30 minutes before serving.

Ice cream fun

If you've got some ice cream in the freezer, it's easy to invent a cool dessert. As the recipes below show, it doesn't have to be complicated, all you need is some fruit, or some chocolate, and a bit of imagination. For the ultimate finishing touch, make a sweet sauce.

For a bit of fun, pipe some whipped cream on top.

Chocolate pears (makes 1)

Spoon vanilla ice cream on to a dessert plate and top with two halves of canned, poached pears in syrup. Spoon over some of the syrup from the can and then drizzle over some chocolate sauce (see recipe opposite).

Fruit sundaes (makes 2)

Place 1 scoop of vanilla ice cream into 2 tall glasses. Mash 8 strawberries with 2 tsp icing sugar and spoon into the glasses. Spoon 2 tbsp strawberry yoghurt into each, then add a mix of fresh fruits such as chopped kiwi fruit, sliced mango, sliced banana, and fresh raspberries. Finish with another scoop of ice cream and some toasted flaked almonds.

Chocolate and hazelnut banana split (makes 1)

Split 1 banana in half and fill with 2 scoops of any ice cream of your choice – vanilla or chocolate-chip ice creams go well. Scatter over some toasted chopped hazelnuts and drizzle with some chocolate or fudge sauce (see recipes opposite).

Chocolate sauce

Break 100 g (3½ oz) dark chocolate into small pieces and place in a saucepan with 4 tbsp hot water, and 45 g (1½ oz) caster sugar. Stir over a low heat until the chocolate has melted, then add 4 tbsp double cream and heat through. Serve warm.

Make chocolate curls with a potato peeler.

Fudge sauce

Put 60 g (2 oz) butter with 60 g (2 oz) light brown sugar in a pan with 2 tbsp golden syrup. Bring to the boil, stirring gently, then boil rapidly for 1 minute. Stir in 120 ml (4 fl oz) double cream and a few drops of vanilla extract. Allow to cool slightly before serving.

For an instant pudding, put a scoop of ice cream on top of a cake, such as a muffin or waffle, and drizzle over some sauce.

Raspberry sauce

Put 350 g (12 oz) fresh raspberries in a food processor with 2 tbsp icing sugar and 1 tbsp fresh lemon juice. Blend until smooth, then pour into a sieve and press the liquid through with the back of a wooden spoon to remove all the pips. You can use this method with other soft berries such as strawberries and blackberries.

Little orange puds

You can also make individual orange-chocolate puddings by grating the zest of 1 orange into the milk and chocolate as it is melting. Then use ramekins instead of one big dish, and cook for 10 minutes less. Decorate with candied orange peel.

To get a really sticky pudding, you need to cook it in a deep dish.

Chocolate pudding

This dessert is cooked in a pan of water, called a bain-marie, which gives a gentler heat. It is best eaten straightaway, while still light and fluffy on top and warm and gooey underneath.

SERVES 4
PREPARATION: 20 MINUTES,
 PLUS COOLING
COOKING: 45–55 MINUTES

200 g (7 oz) dark chocolate,
 broken into pieces
200 ml (7 fl oz) full-fat milk
60 g (2 oz) butter
75 g (2½ oz) caster sugar
2 eggs, separated
60 g (2 oz) self-raising
 flour, sifted
30 g (1 oz) cocoa powder, sifted

1 Preheat the oven to 180°C (350°F/Gas 4). Place the chocolate and milk in a saucepan and heat slowly, stirring until melted and smooth. Allow to cool slightly.

2 Beat together the butter and sugar, then beat in the egg yolks. Fold in the flour and cocoa powder. Add the warm chocolate mixture a little at a time.

3 In a separate bowl, whisk the egg whites until they are firm enough to stand up in stiff peaks.

4 Gently fold the egg whites into the chocolate mixture until they are combined, keeping as much air in the mixture as possible.

5 Spoon the mixture into a deep 1.2-litre (2-pint) ovenproof dish and place the dish in a roasting pan. Half fill the pan with water so it surrounds the dish.

6 Bake for 30–35 minutes, then cover loosely with foil and bake for a further 15–20 minutes. Serve while still warm and gooey.

Tiramisu

The name of this Italian dessert means "pick me up", and the delicious mix of cream, chocolate, and coffee layers certainly will give you a lift! You need to chill tiramisu for a few hours before you eat it, to bring out the flavours.

Top Tip
You can also assemble the tiramisu ingredients in four glasses or bowls to make individual desserts.

SERVES 4
PREPARATION: 20 MINUTES, PLUS CHILLING

60 g (2 oz) dark chocolate
225 g (8 oz) mascarpone
225 g (8 oz) fromage frais
60 g (2 oz) caster sugar
1 tsp vanilla extract
200 ml (7 fl oz) decaffeinated coffee, made with 1 tbsp instant decaffeinated coffee
20 sponge fingers
2 tsp cocoa powder

 1 Grate the chocolate using a grater or food processor. Beat the mascarpone, fromage frais, caster sugar, and vanilla extract together in a bowl until smooth and creamy.

 2 Spoon a third of the mixture into the base of a serving bowl and spread it over evenly with the back of a wooden spoon.

 3 Pour the coffee into a shallow bowl. Dip the sponge fingers into the coffee, and put a layer of them on top of the mixture in the serving bowl.

4 Sprinkle over 1 tbsp of the grated chocolate. Spoon half the remaining mascarpone mixture onto the chocolate-covered sponge fingers and smooth over gently. Top with another layer of dipped sponge fingers, and drizzle over any remaining coffee.

5 Sprinkle over 1 tbsp of the chocolate. Finish with the remaining mascarpone mixture, smoothing over the top evenly. Sift with cocoa powder and sprinkle with the remaining chocolate. Chill in the fridge for 2–3 hours.

The slightly bitter cocoa powder contrasts with the sweet creamy layers below.

Fruity tiramisu

For a lower-fat fruit tiramsu, beat 250 g (9 oz) low-fat fromage frais with 150 ml (5 fl oz) 0% fat Greek yoghurt and 3 tbsp honey. Dip 10 sponge fingers in 150 ml (5 fl oz) orange juice and layer them up in dessert glasses with the fromage frais mixture and a layer of diced nectarines or mangoes. Scatter toasted flaked almonds on top.

In Britain crumble is traditionally served with custard.

The sugary fruit gets very hot, so leave the crumble to cool for 10 minutes before serving.

A feast of fruits
You can replace the fruits in this recipe with whatever is in season. In the summer months, try gooseberries, nectarines, peaches, or apricots, and mix with some soft fruits such as raspberries or redcurrants. In late summer or early autumn, use plums or pears.

Fruit crumble

This easy-to-make dessert has long been a British favourite. Served with cream, ice cream, or yoghurt, a simple fruit crumble tastes delicious, and fruits such as apples and blackberries are a good source of vitamins.

Top Tip
For a crunchy topping, replace 50 g (1¾ oz) of the flour with oats. Just stir them into the crumble mixture with the sugar at the end of step 3.

SERVES 6
PREPARATION: 20 MINUTES
COOKING: 30 MINUTES

For the filling
4 cooking apples
250 g (8 oz) blackberries
60 g (2 oz) granulated sugar
½ tsp ground cinnamon

For the topping
200 g (7 oz) plain flour
100 g (3½ oz) unsalted
  butter, diced
100 g (3½ oz) caster sugar
1 tbsp soft light brown sugar

1 Preheat the oven to 190°C (375°F/Gas 5). Peel the apples, then cut into quarters. Carefully remove the cores and cut into bite-sized pieces.

2 Place the apples and blackberries in a baking dish and sprinkle over the sugar and cinnamon. Stir the fruits to ensure they are coated evenly in the sugar mixture.

3 Tip the flour into a mixing bowl and add the diced butter. Rub the butter into the flour, using your fingertips. When the butter is evenly mixed through the flour and the mixture starts to clump together, stir in the caster sugar.

4 Scatter the crumble topping over the fruits and sprinkle the brown sugar on top.

5 Place the dish on a baking tray and bake for about 30 minutes, or until golden and the fruit juices bubble around the edges.

If fresh *blackberries* are not available, you can use canned, but drain off the juice.

Profiteroles

These light chocolatey balls, filled with cream look very professional, but don't let this put you off. The crispy shells are made of choux pastry, which is easy to make, and even easier to eat.

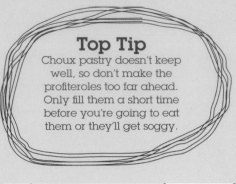

Top Tip
Choux pastry doesn't keep well, so don't make the profiteroles too far ahead. Only fill them a short time before you're going to eat them or they'll get soggy.

MAKES 12
PREPARATION: 30 MINUTES
COOKING: 25 MINUTES

75 g (2½ oz) plain flour
1 tsp sugar
150 ml (5 fl oz) water
60 g (2 oz) butter, plus extra
  for greasing
2 eggs, beaten

For the filling
300 ml (10 fl oz) double cream

For the sauce
150 g (5½ oz) dark chocolate
50 g (1¾ oz) butter

1 Set the oven to 200°C (400°F/ Gas 6). Grease a baking tray. Sift the flour into a bowl with the sugar.

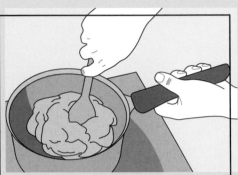

2 Put the water and butter in a pan over a medium heat. When the butter has melted and the mixture begins to boil, take off the heat. Quickly tip in the flour and sugar and beat with a wooden spoon until the pastry forms a smooth ball. Allow to cool for 1–2 minutes.

3 Add the beaten eggs a little at a time, thoroughly mixing them in before adding more, to make a thick, smooth, glossy paste.

4 Hold the greased baking tray under cold running water for a few seconds, then shake to leave it slightly damp. Then place walnut-sized spoonfuls of the mixture on the tray, leaving lots of space between them.

5 Bake in the oven for 25 minutes, or until the pastry is light, puffy, and golden. Put on a wire rack to cool and pierce the side of each pastry with a fork to let out the steam, to prevent them from going soggy.

6 To make the chocolate sauce, break the chocolate into small pieces and put it in a pan with the butter. Melt over a low heat, stirring until melted, and take off the heat.

Try using ice cream instead of cream to fill the pastry balls. Keep them in the freezer until ready to serve, then add the chocolate sauce.

7 Whisk the cream until it forms soft peaks. Cut open the profiteroles and fill each one with cream. Arrange on a serving plate and pour over the chocolate sauce.

Chocolate éclairs
You can also turn choux pastry into éclairs. To make a piping bag, spoon the mixture into a freezer bag and cut off a corner. Squeeze short lengths on to a baking sheet, then bake at 200°C (400°F/Gas 6) for 20–25 minutes. Cut in half, lengthways, cool, fill with cream, and top with chocolate sauce.

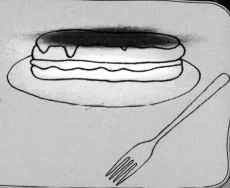

Cherry cheesecake

A perfect summer treat, this no-cook cheesecake is really easy to make and is as tasty as it looks. Make sure you prepare it the day before you want to eat it though – it needs to chill overnight.

SERVES 12
PREPARATION: 30 MINUTES,
PLUS CHILLING OVERNIGHT

250 g (9 oz) digestive biscuits
100 g (3½ oz) butter, plus extra
  for greasing
600 g (1 lb 5 oz) full fat
  soft cheese
100 g (3½ oz) icing sugar
4 lemons, finely grated zest only
1 tsp vanilla extract
300 ml (10 fl oz) double cream
400 g (14 oz) can pitted
  black cherries

If you don't have digestive biscuits, use any plain sweet "oaty" or wholemeal biscuits.

1 Grease and line the bottom of a 23-cm (9-in) loose-based tin with some butter and baking parchment. Put the biscuits in a food bag, seal, and then crush them into crumbs using a rolling pin.

2 Melt the remaining butter in a pan over a low heat, then add the crushed biscuits, and mix until the crumbs are completely coated. Tip the mixture into the tin, pressing down firmly to create an even layer. Chill in the fridge for about 1 hour to set firmly.

3 Mix the soft cheese, icing sugar, lemon zest, and vanilla extract in a bowl, then beat with an electric mixer until smooth. Add the double cream and continue beating the mixture until smooth.

4 Pour the mixture on to the biscuit base, spreading it out evenly with the back of a wooden spoon or spatula. Leave in the fridge overnight.

5 Drain the juice from the cherries into a saucepan. Bring the juice to the boil and simmer for 10 minutes, or until syrupy. Leave to cool.

6 Bring the cheesecake to room temperature about 30 minutes before you want to serve it. Use a spatula to remove it from the tin and paper and carefully slide it on to a serving plate. Pile the cherries on top and spoon over a little of the sauce before serving.

Make sure you use pitted cherries for the topping.

For a professional finish, slice the cheesecake before topping with the cherries.

Fruity variations
If you prefer, you can replace the cherries with other canned fruits, such as raspberries or blackberries, or instead just top your cheesecake with fresh fruits, such as sliced kiwi fruits, strawberries, or blueberries.

Drink up!

Feeling thirsty? Then look no further than this yummy assortment of thirst-quenching drinks. Whether you fancy something cool and fruity for a hot summer's day, or a warming winter hot chocolate, there is something for everyone here, so get guzzling!

Homemade lemonade (serves 4)

Peel the zest from 4 lemons and place in a bowl with 750 ml (1¼ pints) boiling water and 115 g (4 oz) caster sugar. Put to one side for a couple of hours until cool. Remove the strips of zest and add the squeezed juice from the lemons. Ladle into glasses with a handful of ice cubes. If the flavour is too sharp, dilute with chilled sparkling water for a really refreshing treat.

Strawberry and banana smoothie (serves 2)

Spoon 300 ml (10 fl oz) natural yoghurt into a blender. Add about 250 g (9 oz) strawberries, 1 chopped banana, and 1 tbsp honey. Whizz until smooth, then pour into glasses. For a really chilled smoothie, add some ice. To invent your own smoothies, add your favourite fruits to the basic yoghurt and banana mix.

Berry milkshake (serves 2)

Place 1 sliced banana in a blender with 60 g (2 oz) raspberries and 60 g (2 oz) blueberries. Add 250 ml (8 fl oz) chilled milk, and a 150-g (5-oz) pot of strawberry or black cherry yoghurt. Whizz together well, then pour into 2 long glasses and top with extra fruits.

For a healthier milkshake, use low-fat yoghurt.

Non-alcoholic sangria (serves 6)

This classic drink is found all over Spain, with many different regional variations. This recipe uses red grape juice instead of red wine. Pour 1 litre (1¾ pints) chilled red grape juice into a large jug, and add the freshly squeezed juice from 2 oranges and 2 lemons. Top up with 250 ml (8 fl oz) chilled lemonade and add some sliced oranges and lemons. Serve each with a sprig of mint, a slice of lemon, and lots of ice.

Add different fruits, such as chopped apples and halved strawberries, to the sangria for a fruitier punch.

Sweet lassi (serves 4)

This cooling yoghurt drink is popular all over India and Pakistan. To make it yourself, put 400 ml (14 fl oz) natural yoghurt in a jug and stirring in about 200 ml (7 fl oz) chilled water and 2 tsp sugar. Put some crushed ice in 4 long glasses and pour over the lassi mixture. If you like, add some crushed cardamom seeds.

Luxurious hot chocolate (serves 4)

Pour 600 ml (1 pint) milk into a saucepan followed by 100 g (3½ oz) dark chocolate. Cook over a medium heat, stirring constantly, until the chocolate has melted. Bring the mixture to the boil, then whisk in 2–3 tbsp double cream until frothy. Test for sweetness, add sugar to taste, then pour into mugs.

Crush cardamom seeds in a pestle and mortar.

89

Bake-off

Baking is like magic. You mix together a few ordinary-looking ingredients, put them in the oven, and they turn into something extraordinarily delicious – a soft, chewy loaf of bread, a crisp, savoury pizza, or a sweet, crumbly pastry that melts in the mouth. Mmm.

Bread rolls

Bread is easy and cheap to buy, so why bake your own? Simple, because there is nothing quite like the smell and taste of fresh bread, still warm from the oven. But it's also great fun to make, as you mix and shape the stretchy dough and see it rise.

MAKES 12 ROLLS
PREPARATION: 20 MINUTES,
 PLUS PROVING
COOKING: 15–20 MINUTES

1 x 7 g (¼ oz) sachet dried yeast
400 ml (14 fl oz) warm water
650 g (1 lb 7 oz) strong white
 bread flour
1 tsp salt
1 tsp sugar
15 g (½ oz) butter
extra flour, for dusting
olive oil, for greasing

1 Sprinkle the yeast over the water in a jug and set aside for 10 minutes, or until it starts to froth. Mix the flour, salt, and sugar together in a bowl, then rub in the butter with your fingers.

2 Add the water and yeast to the flour mixture and combine with your fingertips, until it forms a soft dough. If it's a bit sticky, add a little more flour.

3 Bring the dough together into a ball and knead on a floured work surface for 10 minutes. Use the heel of your hand to squash it away from you. Fold over the top, turn, and repeat until you have a smooth and elastic dough.

4 Place the dough in an oiled bowl, cover with oiled cling film and a cloth, and set aside for 30–40 minutes to prove (rise), or until the dough has doubled in size.

For a loaf, shape the dough into a large ball at step 5 and place in an oiled 900-g (2-lb) loaf tin. Prove, then bake for 30–40 minutes.

5 Knock back the dough and knead it again for 5 minutes. Divide it into 12 pieces and shape each into a roll. Place them on a baking tray lined with baking parchment. Cover with oiled cling film, and leave for 1 hour, or until doubled in size. Meanwhile, preheat the oven to 220°C (425°F/Gas 7).

6 Sprinkle some flour over the rolls, then bake for 15–20 minutes until golden. You can tell if the rolls are cooked by tapping the bases – if they sound hollow, they're done, if not, pop back in the oven for a few minutes.

For a bit of decoration, sprinkle the rolls with some sunflower or poppy seeds before baking.

Design a dough

Why not experiment and add some different flavours to your rolls? Mix in some chopped fresh herbs, garlic, olives, or even sun-dried tomatoes in step 2, for Mediterranean-style rolls.

Homemade pizza

Instead of ordering a pizza, why not make your own? Just adapt the recipe for bread dough to make the bases, then pile them up with toppings! Try one of these classic Italian recipes or create your own with your favourite ingredients.

Always tear basil. Chopping turns the leaves black, and they will release less flavour.

Pizza base (makes 4)

Follow the recipe for bread dough (see pages 92–93), but use 2 tbsp olive oil instead of butter. Divide the dough into 4 balls. Preheat the oven to 220°C (425°F/ Gas 7). Roll each ball out into a 25-cm (10-in) pizza base and place each on a greased baking tray. Spread each base with a thin layer of passata (puréed and sieved tomatoes) and then your toppings. Season with salt and freshly ground black pepper, then cook in the oven for 10–12 minutes until crisp.

Fiorentina

Divide 175 g (6 oz) cooked, drained, and chopped spinach, ¼ tsp grated nutmeg, 1 tsp thyme leaves, and 250 g (9 oz) sliced mozzarella cheese between the 4 pizza bases. Crack an egg in the middle of each and sprinkle with some freshly grated Parmesan cheese.

Margherita

Divide 250 g (9 oz) sliced mozzarella cheese across the 4 pizza bases. Scatter each with torn fresh basil leaves. Garnish with more basil after cooking.

Capricciosa

Divide between the 4 pizza bases 250 g (9 oz) sliced mozzarella cheese, 8 sliced artichoke hearts, 4 sliced tomatoes, 4 thinly sliced mushrooms, 115 g (4 oz) chopped ham, and 4 tbsp pitted black olives.

You can buy artichoke hearts in a can or jar marinated in herbs, garlic, and oil.

You can swap Dolcelatte with Gorgonzola and ricotta with a *soft goat cheese.*

Gorgonzola

goat cheese

Quattro formaggi

Over the 4 pizza bases, divide 125 g (4½ oz) mozzarella, 30 g (1 oz) freshly grated Parmesan, 125 g (4½ oz) Dolcellate, and 100 g (3½ oz) ricotta. Sprinkle each with a pinch of dried oregano.

Calzone

Make any pizza into a calzone (folded pizza) by keeping the topping away from the edges. Then brush the rim with beaten egg and fold over each base to enclose the filling, pressing the edges together with your fingers. Brush with olive oil, then bake in a preheated oven for 15–20 minutes.

Use a fork to crimp the *edges.*

Lemon tart

This classic dessert often features on the menus of top restaurants, but it's easy to make yourself at home. The rich, buttery base and silky-smooth fresh filling make a winning combination.

SERVES 8
PREPARATION: 25 MINUTES
COOKING: 50–60 MINUTES,
PLUS CHILLING

For the crust
350 g (12 oz) plain flour, plus extra for dusting
175 g (6 oz) butter, chilled and cubed
85 g (3 oz) caster sugar
2 eggs, beaten

For the filling
5 eggs
175 g (6 oz) caster sugar
4 unwaxed lemons, zest and 150 ml (5 fl oz) squeezed juice
250 ml (8 fl oz) double cream

1 Sift the flour into a large bowl. Rub in the butter using your fingertips until the mixture looks like crumbs.

2 Stir in the sugar and beaten eggs. Then use your fingertips to bring all the ingredients together into a soft ball of dough. Wrap the dough in cling film and chill in the refrigerator for 30 minutes.

3 Preheat the oven to 200°C (400°F/Gas 6). Lightly dust the work surface and a rolling pin with flour. Gently roll out the dough into a large thin circle, turning the dough clockwise every couple of rolls. If it starts to stick, dust with extra flour.

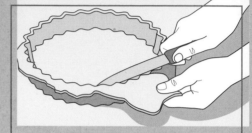

4 Carefully press the pastry into a 23-cm (9-in) loose-bottom tart tin, and trim any excess with a knife. Line the pastry with baking parchment, fill with dried beans, and "bake blind" for 20 minutes (see page 121).

5 When you remove the tin from the oven, turn down the heat to 140°C (275°F/Gas 1). For the filling, whisk the eggs and sugar until combined. Stir in the lemon zest, lemon juice, and then the cream. Pour into the pastry case and bake for 30–40 minutes.

6 Allow the tart to cool and set for at least 30 minutes before slicing and serving.

Short-cut pastry
Homemade pastry is best, but you can cheat by buying a pack of ready-rolled shortcrust pastry, which you can press into the tin at step 4. Or, you can buy a ready-made cooked pastry case and then fill it in step 5.

For a finishing touch, dust the tart with icing sugar and a little extra lemon zest.

Lemon tart is delicious served with cream and fresh berries.

Empanadas

These tasty stuffed pastries are found across Spain, Portugal, and South America, and each region has its own version. Once you know the basic method, you can try different fillings.

Top Tip
Add ½ tsp ground cumin and ½ tsp sweet paprika to the mixture at step 4 for a spicy twist.

MAKES 24
PREPARATION: 30 MINUTES,
  PLUS CHILLING
COOKING: 25–30 MINUTES

For the pastry
450 g (1 lb) plain flour,
  plus extra for dusting
2 tsp baking powder
85 g (3 oz) butter, chilled
  and diced
2 eggs, beaten, plus extra
  to glaze
4–6 tbsp water

For the filling
1 tbsp olive oil
1 onion, finely chopped
4 tomatoes (about
  160 g (5½ oz), chopped
2 tbsp tomato purée
¼ tsp dried chilli flakes
  or powder
200 g (7 oz) can tuna, drained
2 tbsp finely chopped
  fresh parsley
salt and freshly
  ground black pepper

1 Sift the flour and baking powder into a large bowl. Rub in the butter with your fingertips until it looks like coarse breadcrumbs.

2 Add the beaten eggs and the water, a little at a time, mixing them in with a knife, then your fingertips, until a ball of dough is formed. Wrap the pastry in cling film and chill for 30 minutes.

3 Heat the oil in a frying pan and cook the onion over a medium heat for 5–8 minutes, or until soft.

4 Add the tomatoes, tomato purée, chilli flakes, tuna, and parsley, and season with salt and freshly ground black pepper. Reduce the heat and cook for 5–6 minutes, stirring occasionally. Set the mixture aside to cool.

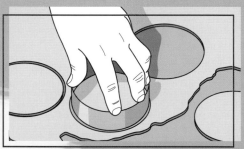

5 Preheat the oven to 190°C (375°F/Gas 5). Roll out the pastry on a floured surface to 3 mm (⅛ in) thick. Use a 9-cm (3½-in) pastry cutter to cut out circles. If you don't have a pastry cutter, you can use a clean can or cup to stamp out circles instead.

6 Put a heaped teaspoon of the filling inside each circle, then brush the edges with water. Fold the pastry over to form a half-moon shape, then firmly crimp the edges to seal.

7 Place the empanadas on a baking tray lined with baking parchment, and brush the tops with beaten egg. Bake for 25–30 minutes, or until golden brown. Serve warm.

These pastry parcels make great picnic food.

Favourite fillings

You can replace the tuna with lots of different fillings. Brown 200 g (7 oz) beef mince in the pan after step 3. Or for a vegetarian version, add 250 g (9 oz) chopped mushrooms and 1 finely chopped garlic clove instead. Cook until any moisture has evaporated, then continue as above.

99

Puff-pastry tricks

Puff pastry is made up of lots of buttery layers that "puff" up when cooked. It's light, crispy, and delicious but tricky and time-consuming to make. The good news is that you can buy it ready-made, chilled or frozen. Sometimes the pastry is already rolled out into a sheet, but it also comes in blocks. There are lots of ways to use it to make quick sweet and savoury treats.

For a touch of fire, before cooking, dust a little paprika over the beaten egg.

Cheese straws
Preheat the oven to 200°C (400°F/ Gas 6). Roll out puff pastry to a rectangle about 0.5 cm (0.25 in) thick. Over half, scatter 60 g (2 oz) grated cheese. Fold over the plain half and roll out again to a rectangle 0.5 cm (0.25 in) thick. Brush with beaten egg and sprinkle with grated Parmesan cheese. Cut into 1-cm (0.5-in) strips, twist each strip several times, and place on a baking tray. Bake for 12 minutes, or until golden.

Tomato and olive tart
Preheat the oven to 220°C (425°F/Gas 7). Place a rectangle of puff pastry about 0.5 cm (0.25 in) thick on to a greased baking tray. Using a knife, score a border 2.5 cm (1 in) from the edges, being careful not to cut all the way through. Spread the centre with 2 tbsp black olive paste and 1 tbsp pesto (see page 61), and cover with slices of tomato and pitted black olives. Brush the border with beaten egg and bake for 20–25 minutes. Scatter with basil leaves to serve.

Invent your own tarts using ingredients such as sun-dried tomatoes, spinach, anchovies, feta cheese, and red onion.

Sausage rolls

Preheat the oven to 200°C (400°F/Gas 6). Roll the puff pastry to a 20-cm (8-in) square 0.5 cm (0.25 in) thick, and cut it in half to get two strips. Spread 2 tsp wholegrain mustard down the middle of each strip. Cut the skins from 450 g (1 lb) sausages and place them in a line on the mustard. Dampen the edge of the pastry with water, fold over, and press the edges together. Cut each half into 8–10 pieces. Brush with beaten egg and cut slits in the top. Bake on a greased baking tray for 20–25 minutes, or until golden.

You can wrap some herbs, or lightly fried onion inside the pastry along with the sausage.

Apple strudel

Preheat the oven to 200°C (400°F/Gas 6). Mix together 3 peeled, cored, and thinly sliced apples, 115 g (4 oz) light brown sugar, 1 tsp ground cinnamon, 100 g (3½ oz) sultanas, and the zest of 1 orange. Place a rectangle of puff pastry on to a lined baking tray. Place the filling down one side and fold the other side of the pastry over, sealing the edges with a little water. Turn the strudel over so the sealed edge is underneath, brush with beaten egg, and bake for 35–40 minutes, or until golden. Sprinkle with icing sugar.

If you like nuts, add 60 g (2 oz) chopped walnuts or pecans to the filling.

Try sprinkling a little ground cinnamon, nutmeg, or mixed spice over the pastry before you roll it up.

Palmiers

Preheat the oven to 200°C (400°F/Gas 6). Roll out the puff pastry to a rectangle about 25 x 30 cm (10 x 12 in) on a sugared surface. Brush with melted butter and sprinkle with 50 g (2 oz) granulated sugar. Roll up one long edge into the middle, then roll in the other edge and press them together. Chill for half an hour, then cut into 1-cm (0.5-in) slices and lay them on a lined baking tray. Bake for 12–15 minutes, or until golden.

Chocolate cake

Treat yourself with this rich and fudgy cake topped with a sticky chocolate icing. The cake will actually improve if you keep it in a tin for a day or two, but it's so delicious it might not last that long!

SERVES 8
PREPARATION: 30 MINUTES
COOKING: 35–40 MINUTES

For the cake
175 g (6 oz) dark chocolate
115 g (4 oz) butter, cubed,
  plus extra for greasing
½ tsp vanilla extract
85 g (3 oz) caster sugar
3 eggs, separated
45 g (1½ oz) self-raising flour
85 g (3 oz) ground almonds

For the topping
115 g (4 oz) dark chocolate
150 ml (5 fl oz) double cream
60 g (2 oz) milk chocolate for
  chocolate curls (optional)

For a lovely rich cake, use dark chocolate with at least 60 per cent cocoa solids.

1 Preheat the oven to 190°C (375°F/Gas 5). Lightly grease and line the base of a deep 20-cm (8-in) cake tin with butter and baking parchment.

2 Break the chocolate into pieces and place in a heatproof bowl above a saucepan of simmering water. Stir until all the chocolate has melted. Add the butter and vanilla extract, and stir until the butter has melted and all the ingredients are combined.

3 Put the sugar and egg yolk in a large bowl, and whisk together until thick, pale, and creamy.

4 Stir the chocolate mixture into the eggs and sugar, sift in the flour, and fold in the ground almonds. Mix until all the ingredients are well combined.

5 Whisk the egg whites in a large bowl until they form stiff peaks. Stir half into the chocolate mixture until smooth and well combined, then gently fold in the rest.

6 Pour the cake mixture into the tin and bake for 35–40 minutes. Cool in the tin for 5 minutes, then turn the cake out on to a wire rack to cool completely.

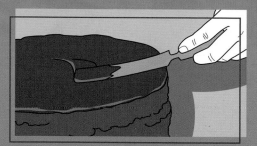

7 To make the topping, melt the chocolate and double cream in a saucepan over a gentle heat, stirring often until it forms a smooth silky icing. Pour on to the cooled cake and smooth over the top and sides with a palette knife. Decorate with grated milk chocolate or chocolate curls (see opposite).

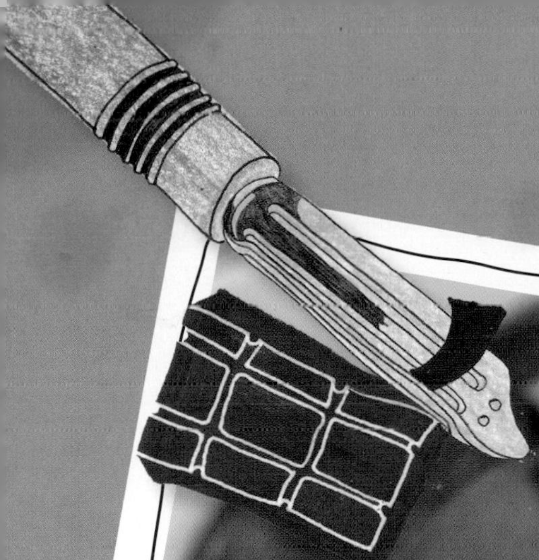

Top T
To make chocolate
a vegetable peele
shave the sides of a
bar. Make sure the c
at room temperature
warm or cold, the
won't form.

Br

A touch of orange

Chocolate and orange is a classic combination, so why not spice up your cake by adding the zest of 1 orange to the cake mixture in step 4, or use orange-flavoured chocolate.

‌ownies

‌hen only something chocolatey will do, these fudgy brownies are just what you need. They make a delicious dessert eaten warm with ice cream, but are also great on their own.

MAKES 12 BROWNIES
PREPARATION: 20 MINUTES
COOKING: 20–25 MINUTES

100 g (3½ oz) unsalted butter, softened to room temperature, plus extra for greasing
200 g (7 oz) dark chocolate
250 g (9 oz) caster sugar
1 tsp vanilla extract
4 large eggs, beaten
75 g (2½ oz) plain flour
60 g (2 oz) cocoa powder

1 Preheat the oven to 180°C (350°F/Gas 4). Grease and line a rectangular cake tin (about 15 x 25 cm/6 x 10 in) with a little butter and baking parchment.

2 Break the chocolate into pieces and place in a heatproof bowl. Rest the bowl over a saucepan of simmering water for a few minutes, stirring until the chocolate has melted.

3 Beat together the butter, sugar, and vanilla extract with a wooden spoon or electric hand whisk until pale and fluffy. Beat in the eggs, a little at a time, until they have all been added and the mixture is smooth and creamy.

4 Sift in the flour and cocoa, a bit at a time, whilst stirring the mixture. Pour in the melted chocolate and mix everything together well.

5 Spoon the mixture into the prepared cake tin and bake for 20–25 minutes. It should be crisp on the top but still slightly gooey inside. Leave to cool in the tin for about 10 minutes. Then transfer the brownie in its paper on to a wire rack to cool a bit more before cutting it into squares.

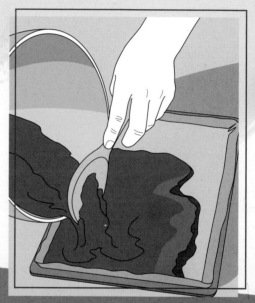

Top Tip

Poke a skewer in the middle of the brownie to test if it is cooked. If it comes out with a slight goo, it's ready! If it still looks like wet cake mixture, put it back in the oven for a few minutes.

Serve warm with ice cream and fresh raspberries for a really yummy dessert.

Go fruit and nuts!

Add some chopped nuts such as pecans, hazelnuts, or Brazil nuts to your brownie mixture before baking. Alternatively, try some dried sour cherries, cranberries, or the grated zest of an orange.

Blueberry muffins

There are countless different muffin flavours, but blueberry is a classic. Light, fluffy, and bursting with berries, these are delicious eaten warm from the oven and are definitely best on the day they are baked.

MAKES 12 MUFFINS
PREPARATION: 20 MINUTES
COOKING: 20–25 MINUTES

250 g (9 oz) plain flour
60 g (2 oz) ground almonds
1 tbsp baking powder
85 g (3 oz) caster sugar
250 ml (8 fl oz) milk
3 eggs, beaten
115 g (4 oz) unsalted
  butter, melted
2 lemons, zest only
175 g (6 oz) fresh blueberries

1 Preheat the oven to 200°C (400°F/Gas 6). Line a 12-case muffin tray with paper cases.

3 Pour the whisked egg mixture into the dry mixture and gently mix them together. Don't overmix – it doesn't matter if the batter is lumpy. The less mixing you do, the lighter the muffins will be. Stir in the blueberries.

2 Sift the flour, almonds, baking powder, and sugar into a large bowl and mix them together. In a separate bowl, whisk together the milk, eggs, melted butter, and lemon zest.

Top Tip
As you add the blueberries, squash them between your thumb and finger so the juice will run out in beautiful purple ripples as the muffins bake.

4 Spoon the mixture into the paper cases, then bake in the preheated oven for 20–25 minutes, or until the tops are golden and firm to touch. Cool in the tin for 5 minutes before transferring to a wire rack to cool completely.

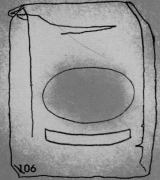

For a crunchy top, scatter over a few flaked almonds and a little sugar before baking.

Mix 'n' match mixture

If you fancy a bit of chocolate in your muffins, add 75 g (2½ oz) white chocolate chunks to the mixture with the blueberries. You can also swap the blueberries for chopped strawberries, blackberries, or diced peaches.

Decorate the cake with a little orange peel or some whole nuts.

Flour power
Use wholemeal self-raising flour instead of white flour if you like - it will give the cake a lovely nutty flavour.

Carrot cake

Putting carrots in a cake might sound strange, but don't knock it until you've tried it! They make the cake scrumptiously moist and sweet. This version also has a hint of spice and is topped with a tangy soft-cheese icing.

SERVES 8
PREPARATION: 25 MINUTES
COOKING: 25–30 MINUTES

For the cake

140 g (5 oz) self-raising flour

2 tsp baking powder

2 tsp ground cinnamon

1 tsp ground ginger

175 g (6 oz) light brown sugar

60 g (2 oz) chopped pecans or walnuts

60 g (2 oz) raisins

140 g (5 oz) carrots, peeled and grated

150 ml (5 fl oz) sunflower oil, plus extra for greasing

2 large eggs, beaten

2 tbsp fresh orange juice

For the topping

300 g (10 oz) full-fat soft cheese

150 g (5½ oz) icing sugar

1 orange, zest and 2 tbsp juice

1 Preheat the oven to 180°C (350°F/Gas 4) and grease and line the bases of two 20-cm (8-in) round cake tins with a little oil and baking parchment.

2 Mix the flour, baking powder, spices, and sugar in a bowl. Add the nuts, raisins, and carrots, and then stir to mix everything together.

3 In a separate bowl, whisk together the oil, eggs, and orange juice, then fold into the dry ingredients.

4 Divide the mixture between the tins and bake for 25–30 minutes, or until risen and springy to touch. Leave to stand in the tins for 10 minutes, then turn out on to a wire rack to cool.

5 For the icing, beat together the soft cheese, icing sugar, orange zest, and juice until smooth. Sandwich the layers with a third of the icing and spread the rest over the top and sides with a palette knife.

109

Cool cupcakes

Cupcakes are the trendiest treats around. Decorated with exquisite icings and toppings, they often look too good to eat! Make your own with this simple vanilla cupcake recipe, and four fun variations. Always stick to the quantities of basic ingredients in the cake mixture, but you can get creative with fun flavourings and decorations. All recipes make 12 cakes.

Grate some lemon zest on to the tops of the cakes.

Vanilla cupcakes

Preheat the oven to 190°C (375°F/Gas 5). Line a 12-hole cake tin with paper cases. Beat 125 g (4½ oz) butter and 125 g (4½ oz) caster sugar in a bowl until pale and fluffy. Beat in 2 eggs and ½ tsp vanilla extract then fold in 125 g (4½ oz) self-raising flour. Divide between the paper cases. Bake for 15–20 minutes until golden. For the icing, beat 175 g (6 oz) icing sugar with 85 g (3 oz) unsalted butter, ½ tsp vanilla extract, and 1 tbsp milk until creamy. Spread on the cakes and decorate.

Lemon cupcakes

Replace the vanilla extract in the cake mixture with the zest of 2 lemons. Bake as before. While the cakes are in the oven, mix 60 g (2 oz) icing sugar with the juice of ½ a lemon to make a syrup. While the cakes are still warm, make a few holes in the tops with a skewer. Spoon 1 tsp syrup over each cake. Omit the vanilla and milk from the icing mixture and replace with 1 tbsp lemon juice. When the cakes are cool, spread over the icing.

Banana and maple cupcakes

Mash 1 ripe banana and stir into the cake mixture with an extra 30 g (1 oz) self-raising flour and 50 g (1¾ oz) chopped pecans. Bake as before. For the icing, replace the vanilla and 30 g (1 oz) of the icing sugar with 2 tbsp maple syrup. When the cakes are cool, spread over the icing.

Top with sliced strawberries and icing sugar.

Strawberry cheesecake cupcakes

Divide 12 chopped strawberries between the paper cases. Spoon the cake mixture on top and bake as before. For the topping, beat 150 g (5½ oz) icing sugar and ½ tsp vanilla essence into 30 g (1 oz) unsalted butter and 60 g (2 oz) full-fat soft cheese until smooth. When the cakes are cool, slice off the top of each one, spoon on some of the icing, and then put the tops back on.

Sprinkles or sweets are a great way to quickly decorate cupcakes.

Chocolate cupcakes

Replace 30 g (1 oz) of the flour in the cake mixture with the same amount of sifted cocoa powder. Divide between the paper cases, then bake as before. For chocolate icing, add 2 tbsp cocoa powder to the vanilla icing with an extra 1 tbsp milk. Whisk in 60 g (2 oz) melted and cooled dark chocolate. When the cakes are cool, spread over the icing. Decorate with chocolate sprinkles, choc chips, or grated chocolate.

Choc-chip cookies

No one turns down a homemade choc-chip cookie, especially when it's still warm from the oven and gooey inside. You can make these cookies with ready-made choc chips or, even better, take a bar of chocolate and chop it into big chunks.

MAKES 12–15 COOKIES
PREPARATION: 20 MINUTES
COOKING: 10–15 MINUTES

125 g (4½ oz) unsalted butter
175 g (6 oz) light brown sugar
1 egg
2 tsp vanilla extract
200 g (7 oz) plain flour
½ tsp baking powder
100 g (3½ oz) milk chocolate,
   chopped into chunks

1 Preheat the oven to 190°C (375°F/Gas 5). Line 2 large baking trays with baking parchment. Melt the butter in a saucepan over a gentle heat.

4 Sift the flour and baking powder into the mixture, a little at a time, and stir in. Then add the chocolate chunks. Don't worry if it looks sticky.

2 Put the sugar into a large mixing bowl, pour over the melted butter, and beat with a wooden spoon.

3 Beat the egg into the mixture with the vanilla extract until everything is blended together.

5 Drop heaped spoonfuls of the mixture on to the baking trays. Slightly flatten the tops and leave plenty of space between them. Bake in the oven for 10–12 minutes, or until just turning golden brown. Leave to cool down a bit on the trays. Then use a spatula to transfer the cookies to a wire rack to cool and harden a little before tucking in.

Top Tip
If you don't eat all the cookies straightaway, store them in an airtight container to eat the next day. You'll find they go extra fudgy overnight.

Try nuts, candied orange peel, or even dried fruits in your cookie dough.

Cookie sandwich

If you like choc-chip cookies and ice cream, why not be greedy and combine the two? For a really scrumptious treat, sandwich two cookies together with a scoop of chocolate or vanilla ice cream.

Macaroons

Mini-macaroons are back in fashion. Crisp on the outside and chewy on the inside, these chic treats are really easy to make, so why not whip up a batch?

MAKES 12 MACAROONS
PREPARATION: 10–15 MINUTES,
 PLUS SETTING
COOKING: 25–30 MINUTES

115 g (4 oz) ground almonds
200 g (7 oz) icing sugar
2 large egg whites
½ tsp cream of tartar
2 tbsp caster sugar
a few drops of almond essence
12 whole blanched almonds

1 Line a baking sheet with baking parchment. Mix together the ground almonds and icing sugar in a bowl.

2 Whisk the egg whites until they form stiff peaks, then whisk in the cream of tartar and caster sugar until glossy. Gently fold in the almond essence, the ground almond and icing sugar mixture.

3 Place 12 spoonfuls of the mixture on to the lined trays and smooth out with a damp finger to form circles about 1 cm (½ in) thick. Leave enough space between them to allow them to spread.

4 Place 1 almond on each spoonful of mixture and set aside for 30 minutes, or until the outsides are no longer sticky.

5 Preheat the oven to 150°C (300°F/Gas 2). Bake for 25–30 minutes, or until tinged with brown. Leave to cool for 5 minutes and then carefully peel away the baking parchment. Cool completely on a wire rack.

You can drizzle the cooled macaroons with some melted dark chocolate.

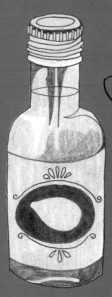

Ginger biscuits

These spicy biscuits smell gorgeous when baking in the oven. It's fun to make them into shapes such as stars or even people, but simple rounds taste just as good!

Top Tip
If you like really gingery biscuits, add another teaspoon of ground ginger to the dough.

MAKES 30
PREPARATION: 20–25 MINUTES
COOKING: 10–12 MINUTES

350 g (12 oz) plain flour, plus extra for dusting

1 tsp bicarbonate of soda

2 tsp ground ginger

115 g (4 oz) butter, plus extra for greasing

175 g (6 oz) light brown sugar

4 tbsp golden syrup

1 egg, beaten

1 Preheat the oven to 190°C (375°F/Gas 5) and line 3 baking trays with baking parchment. Place the flour, bicarbonate of soda, and ginger into a bowl. Add the butter and use your fingertips to rub it in to the flour until it resembles fine breadcrumbs.

2 Stir in the sugar. Add the syrup and beaten egg and mix to form a smooth dough, using your hands to bring the mixture together and knead it lightly.

3 Cut the dough in half and roll out one half on a lightly floured work surface until about 5 mm (¼ in) thick. Use a 7-cm (2¾-in) cutter to cut out rounds. Place them on the lined baking trays, using a palette knife.

4 Repeat with the remaining dough, then bake the biscuits in batches in the oven for 10–12 minutes or until they are a darkish shade of brown. Allow to cool a bit on the trays then use a palette knife to remove them to a wire rack to cool completely.

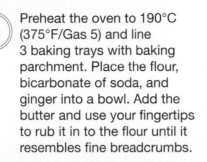

115

Back to basics

There are a few techniques, tips, and tricks that, once you know them, make cooking much easier. This section shows you what you need to know. There's also a guide to the most popular herbs and spices and a glossary to some cookery terms to help you on your way.

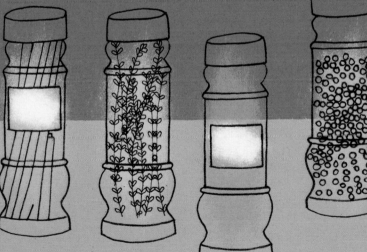

Tricks and tips

A little know-how can help you to achieve the best results and prevent problems in the kitchen. This step-by-step guide shows you some useful techniques that will make cooking easier.

CHOPPING AN ONION

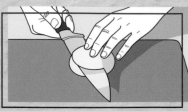

1. Peel the onion, cut it in half, and lay the cut side down. Make a few horizontal slices, cutting up to, but not through, the root.

2. Firmly hold the root end of the onion, then slice down vertically through the layers from the top of the onion to the root.

PEELING A TOMATO

1. Put the tomato in a bowl and pour over boiling water. Leave for 10–20 seconds, then transfer to a bowl of cold water with a slotted spoon.

2. When the tomato is cool enough to handle, peel off its loosened skin with a knife.

CHOPPING GARLIC

1. Slice off the root end of the garlic clove, then loosen the peel by placing the flat side of a knife on top and pressing down firmly.

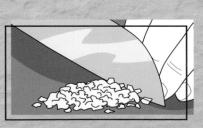

2. Remove the skin, then slice down through the clove into thin slices. For finely chopped garlic, cut across the slices.

PREPARING A CHILLI

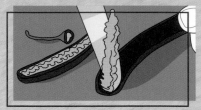

1. Use a small sharp knife to cut off the stalk, then halve the chilli lengthways. Use the tip of the knife to scrape out the seeds.

2. Slice the chilli lengthways into strips, then hold the strips together in a bundle and slice across to get tiny cubes.

Watch out!
The ingredient in chillies that gives them their heat can sting your eyes and skin. Never rub your eyes or nose when handling chillies, and wash your hands and utensils well once you have finished preparing them.

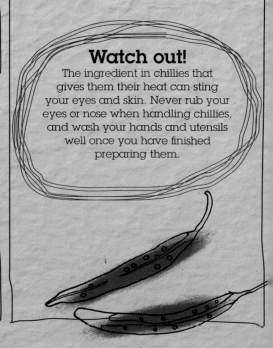

PREPARING DRIED PULSES

1. Soak pulses, such as lentils and beans, overnight in cold water until they have become swollen. The bigger the pulse, the longer it takes to soak.

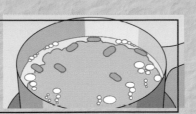

2. Cooking time varies between pulses, and can take between 45 minutes and a few hours. Add a pinch of salt towards the end of the cooking time.

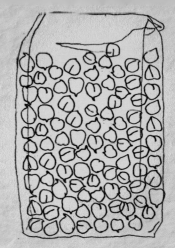

COOKING RICE

1. Allow 75 g (2½ oz) per person. Rinse the rice in a sieve under cold running water, then put it into a large saucepan.

2. Cook the rice in double its quantity of water. Bring to the boil, stir, then lower the heat and simmer for the time given on the packet.

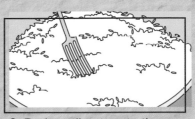

3. Drain well, return to the pan, cover, and leave for 5 minutes. Just before serving, fluff up the rice with a fork to separate the grains.

COOKING DRIED EGG NOODLES

1. Bring a pan of water to the boil. Add the noodles, then bring the water back to the boil. Turn off the heat, cover, and leave for 5 minutes.

2. Drain in a colander and serve. If you are not eating the noodles immediately, run under cold water, drain, and toss them in a little oil to prevent sticking.

BOILING DRIED PASTA

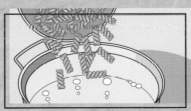

1. Bring a large pan of salted water to the boil. Add the pasta and stir. Boil, uncovered, for the recommended time on the packet.

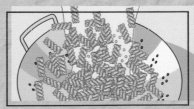

2. Drain the pasta using a colander, gently shaking it to remove any excess water.

MARINATING

1. Using a sharp knife, make shallow cuts into the food that you are marinating, to allow the flavours to seep right in.

2. In a non-metallic dish, mix the food and marinade until well coated. Leave for a minimum of 30 minutes. Meat can be left overnight in the fridge.

Baking techniques

Take the heat out of baking by getting to grips with these basic techniques and terms. Once you know how things are done, you'll find baking a breeze.

RUBBING IN

1. Chop cold butter into small pieces with a knife, then add them to the flour in a large mixing bowl.

2. Take a small quantity of the butter and flour and rub it between your thumbs and fingertips to mix, letting it fall back into the bowl.

3. Continue rubbing in until there are no big lumps of butter left, and the mixture looks like fine breadcrumbs.

FOLDING IN

This is a method of gentle stirring to keep as much air in the mixture as possible. Use a spatula to cut through and turn the ingredients until mixed.

ROLLING OUT PASTRY

1. Sprinkle a little flour onto the work surface and the rolling pin to prevent them sticking.

2. Gently roll the pastry away from your body, then carefully turn it and sprinkle with flour if it sticks. Roll and rotate until you get the right shape.

PREPARING A CAKE TIN

1. Place the cake tin on a sheet of baking parchment and draw around the base. Cut the shape out just inside the pencil line.

2. Use a pastry brush to coat the bottom and sides of the cake tin with a thin layer of melted butter.

3. Put the paper into the cake tin. The melted butter will hold it in place.

BAKING PASTRY BLIND

1. Press the rolled-out pastry into the tin and trim any excess. Prick the base with a fork, then chill for 30 minutes. Line with a sheet of baking parchment.

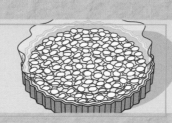

2. Fill with dried beans, or rice, then bake at 200°C (400°F/Gas 6) for 10 minutes. Remove the paper and beans and cook for another 5 minutes.

To test if a cake is cooked, poke a skewer in the middle – if it comes out clean, it's done.

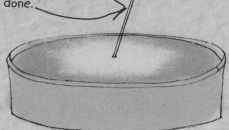

KNEADING DOUGH

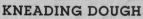

1. Use the heel of your hand to squash the dough away from you, then fold the far edge back over the top and turn the dough a quarter turn.

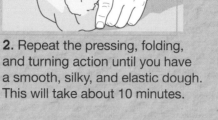

2. Repeat the pressing, folding, and turning action until you have a smooth, silky, and elastic dough. This will take about 10 minutes.

KNOCKING BACK DOUGH

To make sure bread has an even texture, the air is "knocked back" from the risen dough. To do this, simply punch it gently with your fist.

SEPARATING AN EGG

1. Firmly tap the egg on the side of the bowl, insert the tips of your thumbs into the crack, and pull apart, keeping the yolk in one half of the shell.

2. Gently tip the yolk from one half of the shell to the other, letting the egg white fall into the bowl. Put the yolk into a separate bowl.

WHIPPING CREAM

Gently whisk the cream until it thickens and forms soft peaks when the whisk is lifted. Take care not to over-whip or the cream will start to separate.

WHISKING EGG WHITES

1. Put the egg whites into a clean, grease-free bowl. Whisk with an electric hand whisk at medium speed for 1 minute.

2. Turn the speed to high and whisk until the egg whites increase in volume, forming stiff peaks. Do not over-whisk or the egg whites will break up.

MELTING CHOCOLATE

Break the chocolate into a heatproof bowl and set over a pan of gently simmering water. Stir occasionally until melted.

Herbs

In cooking, herbs are the leaves of plants that are added to food. Woody herbs, like rosemary and bay leaves, have strong flavours and you add them to the dish as it cooks. Soft herbs, like basil and parsley, can be eaten raw and should be added just before serving.

Oregano goes really well with pasta and pizza.

Oregano

Coriander

Flat-leaf parsley (left) has a slightly finer and stronger flavour than curly parsley (right).

Cool, refreshing mint is good for serving alongside hot, spicy dishes.

Parsley

There are hundreds of varieties of thyme, each with a slightly different aroma.

Mint

Dill is used a lot in fish dishes.

Dill

Thyme

Chives are the smallest member of the onion family.

Basil

The Greeks and Romans crowned their kings and Olympic champions with wreaths of bay leaves.

Bay leaves

Tarragon is great with chicken.

Tarragon

Fresh or dried?
Woody herbs keep much of their flavour when dried and are worth buying in jars for the storecupboard. Soft herbs, such as basil, parsley, mint, coriander, and chives, don't taste of much when dried so try to use them fresh. Why not grow your own, either in pots or in the garden?

Chives

Rosemary

Spices

Spices are the roots, seeds, buds, fruits, and bark of tropical plants. Some milder spices are used whole, while the more powerful ones are used in ground form, so you can add a pinch or two to flavour your cooking.

Cumin

Saffron is the dried stigmas of the saffron crocus, and is the most expensive spice in the world.

Vanilla is used in baking as pods and as a liquid extract.

Saffron

Vanilla

Nutmeg

Coriander seeds

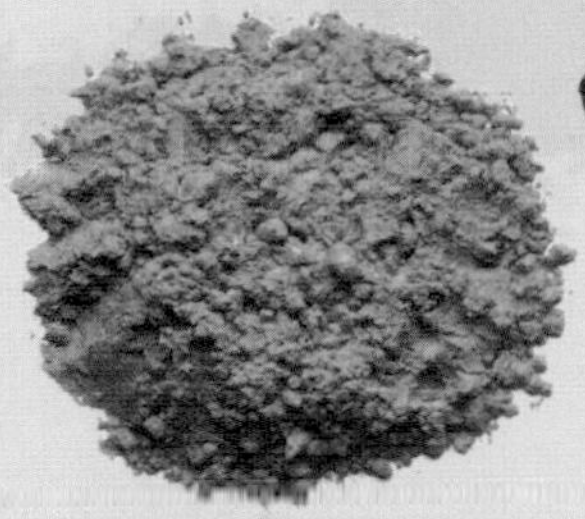

The ground bark of cinnamon is often used in cakes and biscuits.

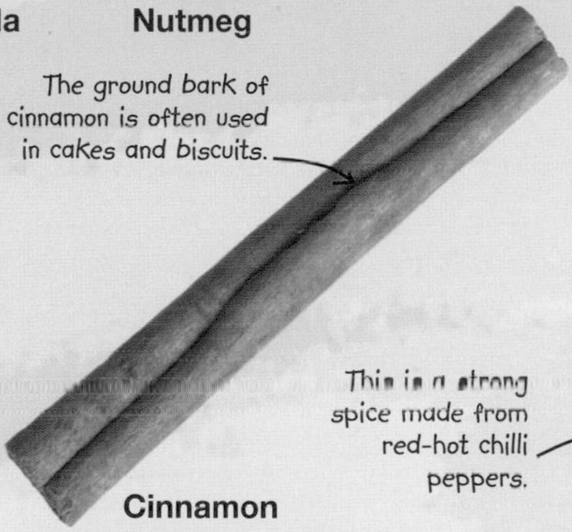

Turmeric

Cardamom

Cinnamon

This is a strong spice made from red-hot chilli peppers.

Cayenne pepper

Ginger is used fresh and dried.

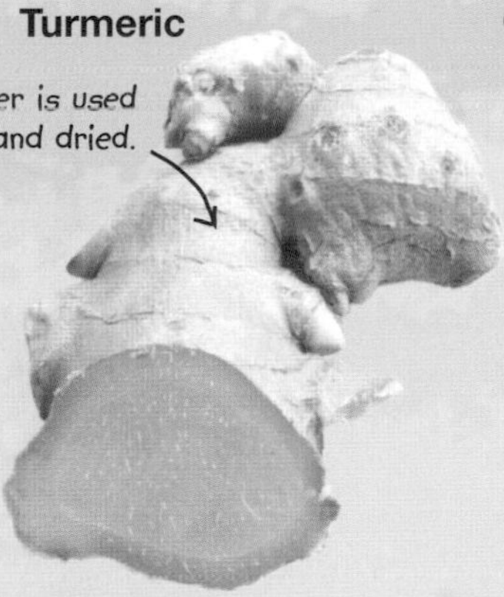

Ginger

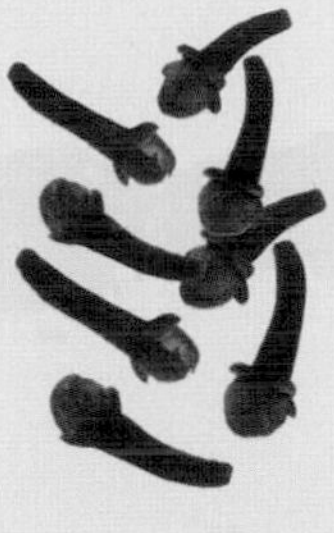

Cloves

Mustard seeds

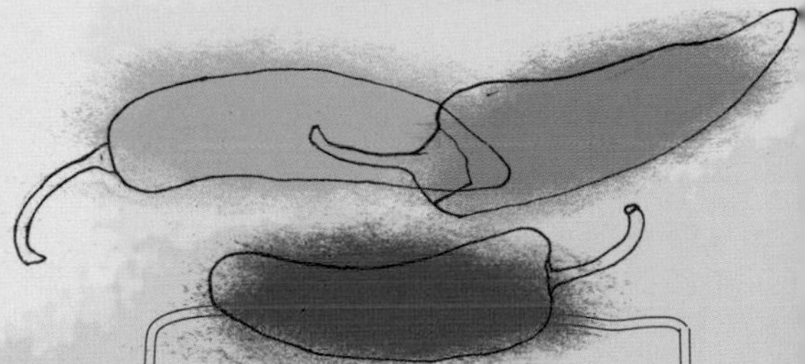

Chillies
The biggest spice crop in the world is chilli peppers. There are hundreds of varieties, ranging from mild and slightly tingling to explosively hot. The hottest fresh chillies are usually the smallest ones with the thinnest skin.

Paprika is made from dried red peppers – it comes in different flavours, from hot to mildly sweet.

Paprika

Black pepper

Glossary

Bain-marie
A dish of water in which you put another dish, containing food, to cook gently.

Bake blind
To cook an empty pastry case lined with paper and dried beans or rice (see page 121).

Baste
To spoon fat over food as it cooks to keep it moist and add flavour.

Batter
An uncooked mixture of flour and liquid, such as pancake mix.

Beat
To stir vigorously, usually with a wooden spoon.

Blend
To mix ingredients together with a spoon. Also, to use a blender to liquidize or purée ingredients.

Brown
To cook food until it turns golden brown in colour.

Caramelize
To heat sugar until it turns brown. Also a term used to describe the sugars in food, such as onions, turning brown when they are heated.

Carbohydrates
One of a group of foods that includes starchy and sugary foods used by the body to make energy.

Concentrate
A solution that is strong in flavour because some of the water in it has been evaporated away.

Cream
To mix together fat and sugar with a wooden spoon to incorporate air into the mix.

Crimp
To fold or pinch together the edges of pastry or dough for decoration, or to seal in the filling.

Curdle
To cause milk or sauce to separate into solids and liquid.

Dash
A small amount of seasoning.

Deseed
To remove and discard the seeds from fruits or vegetables.

Dice
To cut food into small cubes.

Dollop
A large spoonful of food.

Drizzle
To pour a very small amount of liquid or oil over food.

Dry-fry
To cook food in a frying pan without any added fat or oil.

Fibre
The part of plant food that is not digested and passes through the digestive system and out of the body.

Fold
To combine ingredients, by cutting and mixing gently, so as to keep as much air in the mixture as possible (see page 120).

Glaze
To brush a mixture over food either to give it flavour or a glossy finish.

Grate
To rub food on a grater to give fine or coarse shreds.

Griddle
To cook food in a special ridged pan.

Hull
To remove the green leaves and coarse centres of soft fruits.

Knead
To stretch and fold dough until it becomes elastic and smooth (see page 121).

Knob
A small amount of fat – about one teaspoon.

Knock back
To punch risen bread dough to return it to its original size before shaping (see page 121).

Marinade
A liquid that adds flavour and may tenderize food.

Marinate
To leave food in a marinade to flavour and tenderize it.

Mineral
A nutrient found in food that is essential in small amounts to keep the body healthy.

Parboil
To partially cook food in boiling water.

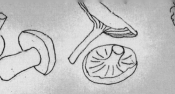

Pinch
The amount of an ingredient that you can pick up between your thumb and forefinger.

Poach
To cook food, such as fish or eggs, in a gently simmering liquid.

Prove
To leave a yeast dough in a warm place to double in size.

Protein
One of a group of foods, such as meat, eggs, pulses, nuts, and seeds, that include ingredients essential for keeping your body strong.

Purée
Food that has been mashed, sieved, or blended in a blender or food processor until smooth.

Reduce
To thicken and intensify the flavour of a liquid by boiling it uncovered so that the excess liquid evaporates.

Rest
To set food aside for a short time – for example, roasted meat is rested so that it becomes moist and tender.

Roast
To cook with a little fat in a roasting tray in the oven.

Rub in
To rub together a flour and fat mixture between your fingers and thumbs until it resembles breadcrumbs (see page 120).

Salmonella
A bacteria that can cause food poisoning.

Sauté
To fry food in a small amount of fat, frequently stirring it so that it browns evenly.

Score
To make shallow cuts over the surface of food.

Seal
To brown the surface of meat in a small amount of hot fat to lock in its juices.

Season
To add salt and pepper, according to taste, to improve or bring out the flavour in a dish.

Set
To leave a soft food to become firm.

Shallow-fry
To cook food in a small amount of fat or oil in a frying pan.

Shred
To tear or cut food into fine strips.

Sieve
To pass food through a fine mesh to remove lumps, add air, or produce a purée.

Simmer
To cook food so that it bubbles gently.

Stand
To put food to one side for a short period of time.

Stir-fry
To cook pieces of food in a small amount of very hot oil, usually in a wok, stirring constantly.

Stock
A liquid flavoured with the meat, fish, or vegetables that were cooked in it, often used to make a soup or sauce. Stock can also be made by adding water to a stock cube.

Syrup
A concentrated solution of sugar and water.

Toast
To cook food until it is golden brown, either under the grill or in a pan.

Vitamin
One of the essential nutrients in food that your body needs to work properly and stay healthy.

Whip/whisk
To beat ingredients, such as cream or egg whites, to add air and make them thicker.

Zest
The thin coloured outer layer of a citrus fruit, which contains flavour in its oils.

Index

Credits

Dorling Kindersley would like to thank:
Jessamy Wood for editorial help, Andrew Leeke for design assistance, Stephanie Pliakas for proofreading, and Jackie Brind for preparing the index.

The publisher would like to thank the following for their kind permission to reproduce their images:

(Key: a-above; b-below/bottom; c-centre; l-left; r-right; t-top)

Corbis: Riou / Photocuisine 101bc. **Dorling Kindersley:** Rough Guides 94cl. **Getty Images:** Foodcollection RF 13bc, 97; FoodPix / Alexandra Grablewski 31bl; Nordic Photos / Janne Hansson 93; Photodisc / Liza McCorkle 111bl; Photographer's Choice / Still Images 85; Photographer's Choice RF / Jamie Grill 64tr; StockFood Creative / Alain Caste 89bl; StockFood Creative / Chris Alack 55; StockFood Creative / Clare Plueckhahn 110tr; StockFood Creative / Ellen Silverman 37cl; StockFood Creative / Evan Sklar 77tl; StockFood Creative / Jorn Rynio 94crb; StockFood Creative / Leigh Beisch 95bl; StockFood Creative / Louise Lister 36tr, 76cl; StockFood Creative / Luzia Ellert 65cl; StockFood Creative / Marc O. Finley 77cl; StockFood Creative / Rita Maas 65bc; StockFood Creative / Sam Stowell 29; StockFood Creative / Ulrike Koeb 18br; UpperCut Images / MIB Pictures 30bl. **iStockphoto.com:** Steve Debenport 113; Giancarlo Polacchini 89tc; Rusm 18-19; travellinglight 45br. **Photolibrary:** FoodCollection 21, 77br. **StockFood.com:** Chris Alack 101tc; Bayside 59; Uwe Bender 88br; Bialy, Dorota i Bogdan 14tr; Rua Castilho 23bl; Jean Cazals 65tr; Hannes Eichinger 70br; Eising 12br; Geoff Fenney 110br, 111tc; Foodfolio 71tr; Louise Hammond 77tr, 100cl; Lara Hata 71br; John Hay 44bl; Marie Jose Jarry 23tc; Dave King 61bl; Jo Kirchherr 70tr; Robbert Koene 74; Laurange 50; Studio Lipov 76tr; Renato Marcialis 101cl; Chugrad McAndrews 25; Gareth Morgans 37br; Karl Newedel 95tc; P. Nilsson 61cr; Stefan Oberschelp 64bl; William Reavell 35; Rob Fiocca Photography 82; J. Rynio 70cl; Bodo A. Schieren 95c; Sam Stowell 49; Teubner Foodfoto 40; Viennaslide / Richter 60cr; Frank Wieder 60cl; Tanya Zouev 111c.

All other images © Dorling Kindersley
For further information see:
www.dkimages.com